A STEP-BY-STEP GUIDE FOR FIRST TIME MOMS

A NURTURING APPROACH TO BABY SLEEP TRAINING

A STEP-BY-STEP GUIDE FOR FIRST TIME MOMS

GHISLAINE D. NNAJI
Pediatric Sleep Consultant

Absolute Author
Publishing House

Absolute Author
Publishing House

Publisher: Absolute Author Publishing House
Editor: Dr. Melissa Caudle

Paperback ISBN: 978-1-64953-232-9
eBook ISBN: 978-1-64953-233-6

DEDICATION

"To all the sweet, little babies who inspired me throughout the years. Because of you, more babies can sleep better!"

TABLE OF CONTENTS

INTRODUCTION i

CHAPTER ONE 1
Preparing/ Shifting Your Mindset

CHAPTER TWO 8
Sleep Training Misconceptions

CHAPTER THREE.. 11
Your Goals And Your Why's

CHAPTER FOUR 15
Good To Know Before Sleep Training

CHAPTER FIVE 27
Predictability: Establishing Predictable Habits

CHAPTER SIX.. 34
Safe Sleeping For Babies Guideline

CHAPTER SEVEN 37
The Overall Baby's Temperament

CHAPTER EIGHT 40
Things To Pay Attention To During Sleep Training

CHAPTER NINE... 71
During Sleep Training

CHAPTER TEN 76
Sleep Training Strategies

CHAPTER ELEVEN 82
Bedtime Strategy

CHAPTER TWELVE 85
Night Wakings Strategy

CHAPTER THIRTEEN 92
Schedules Strategies

CHAPTER FOURTEEN 94

    Obstacles That May Disrupt Sleep Training

APPENDIX 111

INDEX 112

RESSOURCES 115

REFERENCES 116

ACKNOWLEDGMENTS................................118

ABOUT THE AUTHOR................................119

INTRODUCTION

I'm so excited that you are reading this copy and can't wait for you and your precious bundle of joy to finally get the sleep that you so much need and deserve. Sleep is very essential in everyone's life, yet we tend to overlook its impact on our daily activities, goals, achievements, and fulfillment. Having worked with countless moms from different backgrounds and with different parental skills, especially first-time moms, I asked myself what could help a brand new mom, who is learning every parental skill while taking care of a new baby, to thrive and have a smooth new parental experience. Every time I talked to an exhausted mom, I realized that a mom's mindset, a detailed recipe or framework to reach their sleeping goals, and real-life relatable examples were mostly transformative. I like this saying that states that we can do anything only if we had a recipe. For example, if I want to master how to make a lemon ginger cheesecake and to make sure that I won't mess it up and start over and over again, I will have to use a proven recipe to tell me, teach me, and show me what to do at each step. Now, I may not understand why I should include salt in a sweet treat but when the recipe explains why I will be more likely to add that salt. The same thing applies to sleep training. If you tell me to do things that sound advanced or that I'm not sure I'm ready to follow through with my precious baby, I will likely begin to cherry-pick on which method I use and which step to skip, and that leads to not getting the desired results. A bit of my story: I'm Ghislaine Duhujinema Nnaji; a mom, a wife, and a woman who likes to empower exhausted sleep-deprived new moms to stay fierce, stronger and keep their inner rockstar shinning, and to help them address all of their baby troubling sleep habits without having to fail. I'm a firstborn in a family of 5 girls! I was born in Rwanda, and in addition to English, I also speak French, Swahili, and Kinyarwanda. I went to an all-girls school that focused on empowering women to be the best versions of themselves. My mom was not a stranger to that slogan, and she always challenged us to be confident, empowered, and take action. Over time, I developed a passion for empowering moms the way my mom always empowered us. As a firstborn, I was very involved in helping to take care of my little sisters. Like many moms, my mom would get home from work visibly exhausted, and it bothered me. At 12, I began taking charge and tried to impress my mom so that she doesn't have to worry about us at least not for bedtime. I would play with them to burn some energy, I made sure that they ate enough so that mom doesn't have to come back and start over again. I would take them a bath, and I remember they hated me for that part because I wanted it to finish before mom gets home. I eventually became good at taking care of babies without necessarily having a clear structure even though I knew what worked best. It became a great reward for me to see my mom relaxed after work and my sisters intact. Fast forward, when I came to the US while pursuing my Bachelor of Science degree in Public Health, taking care of people was what I knew best. I worked with various direct service institutions as well as other face-to-face settings, and on top of that, I would find myself covering for new parents' date nights; staying with their children so that they could have a bit of "mommy and daddy" time. So this is where the magic happened! Or when I knew I was made for working with babies and empowering new moms. It all started when I would take care of a child for parents' date night, and the next morning they would call me - super excited and amazed- asking me what I did for their baby to sleep better that past night. They would explain how they had been trying to get their baby to sleep better with no success. I would unknowingly use my sleeping methods and tips from when I used to be with my little sisters and by bedtime, a baby was ready to sleep and sleep longer. If a baby usually woke up 4 times a night, they would only wake up once in the morning as they were not used to having a long stretch of sleep. Parents would be very surprised, happy, and wanted to learn more of what I did to have their baby sleep well that night. I would train them to sleep even through the night, and from one parent, I would get recommendations to their friends, sisters, coworkers, and the list grew so big, here I am. I realized that the attitude that a mother brings into motherhood is the one that tends to shape how smooth the process of motherhood will be. For over a decade, I helped many families to sleep through the night by training their babies ranging from 0 to 3 years old, the good and effective sleep habits. I worked with families and equipped them with knowledge on not only what to expect when unexpected situations happen, roadblocks during sleep training, how to manage sleep issues related to new milestones, sleep regressions, teething, frequent night wakings, tantrums before bedtime, addressing short naps as well as night weaning, eliminating sleep props but also on how to calmly and effectively handle those situations without losing their minds. With more experience, tried and tested strategies, and successful stories, I developed a clear structure on how to help more moms all over the world. I incorporated training babies with encouraging them to be more confident, independent, and caring little beings but also helping moms to find that missing piece of the puzzle in fully enjoying motherhood. I encourage you to follow this sleep training guide in its entirety to enjoy the benefits it has to offer, and who knows, you, your baby, and the rest of the household could be sleeping through the night two weeks from now.

Sweet Dreams!

CHAPTER ONE

Preparing/ Shifting Your Mindset

Most of the time, the first few words I hear from exhausted moms are a desire to find a serene sleep for their baby. They wish their baby could sleep soundly without constantly crying and protesting whenever they are in the crib. It feels like a norm now to meet someone in a store, and the first two things they say are, "Aww, your baby is so cute" and "Is she/he a good sleeper" or "How is she/he sleeping?" It's as if everyone expects or has accepted that babies can be tough to be put to sleep, and this makes us moms accept the situation of sleepless nights until we cannot take it anymore. I know you've inquired all over the place about effective sleep training. So, let's not beat around the bush and go straight to the point. As an exhausted mom, the last thing you want is a long book about the history of sleep.

But first things first, babies depend entirely on us, parents, and they sense and feel it when you are not sure of what you are doing or when you are hesitating. They sense it when you are stressed out, and this does not help the situation when trying to keep things calm. When I had my first son and was still in the hospital, I got a phone call from a friend's doctor that she was not feeling well. As we were talking, even though I "tried" to stay calm while talking to the doctor, my one-day-old little son, whom I was nursing, stopped and looked at me with a stare as if he was saying, "are you, ok mom?" At this moment, I quickly composed myself and

1

told the doctor that I will call her back. This showed me how babies could feel their parent's mood.

You are happy and feel very blessed about your beautiful little bundle of joy, and this happiness comes with that unconditional & pure love that you want to give to your baby nothing but the best. All you want is to be perfect for your baby. With this feeling comes anxiety that can put perspectives all over the place.

As a new mom, many changes are going on both in your body and in your family. It's overwhelming to keep it together with a brand new baby, but it helps establish goals for your baby's needs and family's needs. Point out some specific points of what you need to have for your life to go smooth. I will guess a well-rested, happy, healthy baby and a well-rested, happy, healthy mommy and daddy come on the list. Then the rest on the list will fall into place!

But of course, this can be easier said than done. The secret here is the attitude you use in going about these set points. With an optimistic and confident attitude, you will unleash the mother within you.

I noticed that many sleep training issues begin from habits we as parents create, and for young babies, what we teach to them is what they learn. Their brain learns to adapt to every pattern of daily life. They get used to these patterns so much that it is rather hard to change them without protesting. The same way they learn undesirable habits such as refusing to sleep in a crib because they prefer to sleep on mommy or daddy's chest is the same way they can learn good habits such as going to sleep without depending on anything. With habits, though, once they are set in, babies prefer to keep it that way. They do not want change; in fact, babies are not good fans of change.

This is where it becomes vital to implement good habits since changing them later results in protesting babies though the good news is that they can still adjust these habits with effective and tried strategies. When sleep training the baby, our goal is to empower, instill confidence, and develop an independent and kind child using a fair method that doesn't need to overwhelm, frustrate and cause guilt that we abandoned the baby. I realized that the attitude that a mother brings into motherhood is the one that shapes how smooth the process of motherhood will be. Empowering yourself with a can-do attitude of confidence can make a tremendous difference. Calmness and confidence from a parent are pretty contagious to the baby. You find that when you respond to a situation calmly, your baby will respond better than when you look frustrated, overwhelmed, and not sure of what to do.

How about the golden question? **Will my baby cry?**

I can never advise parents to let a baby cry it out. I think it is too harsh. No parents like to hear a crying baby, and tears are often the most push backs for parents who would like to start sleep training. You don't need to let a baby cry for a long time for them to sleep. There are many gentle ways to help your child learn to sleep well and sleep longer without involving harsh methods of letting him cry for hours. You need to learn the baby's behaviors and temperament and strategically adjust your sleep training accordingly. Now, crying is the only way for the baby to show and express their emotions. Like when they see a stranger, their first response may be to cry. When they hear a sudden noise on the street or when you take a toy from them, they may start crying. So, it is not realistic to expect no tears when you change their sleep habits, as it is their only way to say they just want to keep their old ways of sleeping. They would not like to change the comfortable sleep on their mom's or daddy's chest or the prolonged sweet rocking from mommy or daddy that they have been enjoying. So, yes, when you change that, there will be tears, and the older the baby is, the stronger the protesting will be since the baby has his habits set in and bitterly doesn't want to change them. Younger babies catch up pretty quickly as soon as on the first night.

So, what does this show us?

- Babies don't do well with surprises and new situations.
- They prefer predictable situations or a familiar environment.
- They respond well when they know what's coming up next.

3

- To babies, sleep training is a significant change, and we know babies are not good fans of changes.

How do you help them cope with changes?

✓ Use tried and tested approaches to avoid constant changes.

✓ Gently prepare them for the new change.

✓ Take it slowly, and the good thing is that they adapt pretty quickly when the changes are established in a carefully crafted process, and most babies adjust to healthier sleep habits within days.

✓ Seek help from relatives or friends who have gone through the same process and who can share a tip or two with you. This is where the power of communication becomes essential for a new mom. The more you share your concerns and worries with someone, the easier it becomes to navigate and conquer them.

✓ If you still feel stuck, it may be time to seek help from professionals. The professionals with a proven track record of getting families results without the sleepless nights, crying babies, and the exhaustion that many mothers, unfortunately, go through still ending up with no results.

I want to touch a bit on these before getting into **the step-by-step process** to remind you; you can do it! You are not alone; if all the moms that hit their rock bottoms did it, so can you. You are unique in your way and what I want you to know is that you just need to trust your gut. You are a mom, and that alone is powerful! You know inside you; you are trying your best. So, let's start with that best and gradually add to it. As a mom, you don't need to know everything under the sun to consider yourself a wonderful mom; you need a little guidance and (a little push) to remind you; **YOU** can do it and show you how to do it.

THE MOM'S GUILT

Many parents experience an unshakeable feeling of guilt when they sleep train their babies. As a loving mom, you indeed feel bad hearing your little one cry. It is a natural feeling, and every parent out there knows how difficult it is not to break the routine to soothe those big, watering eyes.

As hard as it may be, try to remain focused on implementing a healthy sleep pattern for your baby. Babies may wake up several times per night crying. If you rush in to ease your child at the very first noise she makes, you will take away her chance to learn how to fall back asleep on her own.

Soothing your child every second she's fussy during sleep training will make it hard to learn how to self-soothe so that they can become independent sleepers. Of course, in the short term, you stop them crying and relieve yourself of guilt. Unfortunately, in the long-term, you induce a lifetime of resting problems, sleep deprivation, behavioral issues, and learning troubles.

Think about what kind of mother you want to be for your baby. You wouldn't like to be a parent who gives up at the slightest squeal and cannot be consistent in implementing something as beneficial as sleep. Your baby deserves your strong and confident nature, which will help you lovingly establish safe and healthy boundaries. Bring out that inner mom you wish to be. It will surprise you by how smooth things will start going once you gain your confidence back and when you allow the rockstar mom to prevail.

Let me guess how you may be feeling right now or what you are likely going through. I know: You will freak out by how much I know of what you may be experiencing. But this is to show you; you are not alone in whatever overwhelm you are going through.

- Your baby is constantly crying, cranky and fussy.
- The baby won't sleep longer than two to three hours at night.
- You sit on the floor, wondering what could be wrong with your baby.
- You sometimes get anxious and frustrated about why you are not doing it right.

- You feel like a failure that you can't get your baby to sleep well.
- The laundry is piling up.
- Dishes in the kitchen sink look like they never end.
- You can't remember the last time you had a pedicure.
- The house is always messy and looks like it can never get back in order.
- Your only refuge is that quick three-minute shower before the baby wakes up again.
- You can't remember when last you slept at least five hours straight.
- You and your partner are becoming like roommates and can't find quality time to enjoy each other's company.
- By the time you get to bed, he had waited for you for ages and fell asleep, and it has become the story of your life.
- That weird silence at home when both of you are at home and can't recognize each other anymore.
- You feel lost and feel you are the only one doing something wrong.
- You can't express your fears, not even to your mom or best friend, because you feel ashamed.
- You are at the brick of divorce.
- You feel embarrassed because you aren't able or can't get over that you are not keeping your home in order.
- Your partner gets home, and you just started preparing dinner, you have not changed out of your PJs, and the house is a mess, which creates tension in your marriage/relationship.
- Too many what if (s), e.g., what if I did this, what if I did that? Depression because you are worried the baby is not doing well the way you want him/her to be.
- Constant and endless exhaustion.
- You feel you are constantly giving but not getting your expected reward despite you trying hard. A reward of having a happy, sleeping & well-rested baby, happy marriage, time for yourself, connecting with friends, cuddling on the couch with your partner/spouse, time to watch your favorite show, time to get your work done, having a date night.
- And so on.

ON BEING PERFECT

Enjoy your uniqueness and focus on recognizing and rewarding your effort to help your baby be a good sleeper. Once you understand you are a good mom just as you are, that you don't have to be like the other mom you met at Starbucks or the park, you will realize how good a mom you are to your little bundle of joy. You don't need to be perfect to be a good mom. Motherhood is a unique learning process, and your uniqueness brings in a sweet and special flavor to it. Be fierce, be confident, follow your "mommy" instincts, accept to seek help when you feel stuck, be vulnerable when you hit that rock bottom. Recognizing vulnerability is a good strength that is overlooked but helps us get back on our feet. We worry about what others will say or think about our parenting style and forget that everyone has their vulnerabilities. The more aware we are of those weaknesses and vulnerabilities, the clearer the vision toward resolving the issues, and the more confident and empowered we will be about ourselves. And confidence with motherhood does the magic!

CHAPTER TWO

Sleep Training Misconceptions

Below are some things that may make it hard for you to get your baby to sleep well successfully.

- You keep thinking that putting in boundaries will cost you.
- You hear or fear that sleep training does not work and that it takes forever.
- You think that sleep training means baby crying for the entire night.
- You quietly tell yourself that you may be selfish and want to feel better (but you know what you want is your baby to sleep better).
- On social media, you constantly hear people say that they did this, they did that, and wonder why that's not working for you. This is because some social media feeds can mislead or don't give the details or their difficult moments before reaching their results.
- Too many stories and methods you have been told.
- We feel like it's ridiculous to hire someone or ask someone to help our baby have one of the most important things for his/her mental, physical, and emotional development; sleep, yet we find it ok to hire or seek help for fixing a broken faucet.
- Society's expectations: In society, people expect moms to be like these supernatural humans who can deal with everything. While

moms are strong and can deal with pretty much everything, it does not happen overnight. It's a learning process we should accept to learn to be where we want to be, eventually.

Society's misconception makes us believe we need to hit rock bottom before seeking help, and help can come from anyone who can listen and understand us. This can be a sister, a best friend, another mom at your baby's "rhymes class" (music class) or yoga studio, a coworker, a mentor or other experienced professionals, and of course, your partner. I left the partner for last on purpose. Often, moms expect their partners to see or feel what they are going through, be it emotionally, mentally, or physically. As much as the partners would love to assist, they, unfortunately, may not be aware of what you are going through, especially if they don't spend the entire day with you. It is crucial to ask for help, share your concerns and seek advice when you feel stuck. There is nothing more relieving than knowing that someone feels your struggles and that they have your back.

Benefits of sleep training your baby:

- You will confidently be able to set boundaries.
- It will help you bring out that inner mom that you have always wanted to be.
- You will gain more self-esteem.
- You will stop pretending this way is working and living that way is truly working in your home, your life, in your daily goals, your habits, and so on.
- You may get back in shape because now you have time to take care of yourself.
- That sense of self-worth since you feel you are fulfilling your goals as a mother.
- Restored marriage and stronger bond since you can spend more time together and plan for date nights without worrying that only mommy can put the baby to sleep.
- Your mind becomes free, sharp to do more other things that you had been postponing.

- That sense of freedom and you don't have to worry about the baby waking up after forty minutes, and you can predict the baby's daily schedule as well as yours.
- You get your life back.
- You, your baby, and your entire family can smile again.

CHAPTER THREE

Your Goals And Your Why's

WHAT ARE YOUR WHY'S?

Put down the reasons you want to sleep train your baby. What does it mean for you, your baby, your spouse, your work, and your family?

Below are a few reasons; add on the ones that resonate with you and your unique family situation.

YOUR BABY:

1. Because you want her to gain a lifetime of healthy sleep habits.
2. Because it will improve and maintain your baby's overall health.
3. Because it will make her become more independent and happily sleep in her crib.
4. Because it decreases the risk of sleep deprivation and other related side effects.
5. Because it cultivates a lifetime feeling of discipline.
6. Because she will cry less in the long run and be a happy baby overall.
7. Because it will teach her the benefits of self-soothing.
8. Because it will help her develop healthy eating and digestion rhythms.

11

9. Because it makes it easier to leave her with others (grandparents, babysitters, older siblings).
10. Because it is more likely for her to develop into a healthier and happier adult.

MOM:

1. Because it will improve mom's health.
2. Because it will reduce or eliminate constant exhaustion.
3. Because it will minimize the risk of postpartum depression.
4. Because it will ensure a predictable schedule.
6. Because it will improve your mood and confidence.
7. Because it allows you to take time for household activities and chores as well.
8. Because it puts you in control of your baby's health and sleep condition.
9. Because it gives you extra time for leisure activities, physical activities, date nights, and more.
10. Because an in-control, healthy, and happy mom makes a great partner for her husband.

DAD:

1. Because it helps him play an important part in the baby's sleep.
2. Because it makes him feel useful and important at this stage of the baby's life.
3. Because it helps him focus on work and household duties better.
4. Because it improves his mood and confidence.
5. Because it gives him a goal to follow and reach.
6. Because it provides him with a predictable schedule.
7. Because it makes him feel in control.
8. Because it provides him with a sense of order and peace of mind.
9. Because it improves his health and happiness.
10. Because a healthy and happy dad makes a great partner for his wife.

YOUR FAMILY:

1. Because it helps everyone get the rest that they need.
2. Because it improves the general mood in the household.
3. Because everyone can get in line with a pre-set schedule.
4. Because it supports long-term organizing of chores and duties for all family members.
5. Because it helps everyone in the house cope better with this period.
6. Because there will be fewer crying noises in the house in the long run.
7. Because it gives the baby's siblings a sense of order and organization.
8. Because it helps everyone figure out quickly when something is wrong.
9. Because it enables the family to plan trips and events around the baby's sleep needs.
10. Because it allows mom and dad to spend more time together.

YOUR WORK :

1. Because it allows you to focus on your work when resuming your pre-pregnancy job.
2. Because it gives you time to look for a new job in the postpartum period.
3. Because it helps you focus on your lifelong career.
4. Because it gives you small-time windows to work on minor projects.
5. Because it will help you balance family time and work time quickly.

6. Because it will make it easier for you and the baby once your job resumes and daycare starts.
7. Because you will leave your baby with others safely and go to work.
8. Because it will reduce the time you have to stay at home before resuming work.

9.   Because it will give you time to reconsider your financial situation.
10. Because it will teach you about kids and help you decide if you want to have more or just focus on your career.

ADD YOUR WHY'S BELOW

....
....
....
....
....
....
....
....
....
....
....
....
....
....

CHAPTER FOUR

Good To Know Before Sleep Training

BABY CRYING DIFFERENTIATIONS

Young babies possess only one form of communication. Unfortunately for most parents out there, that form is crying. You can't blame the baby, though. She just arrived in a new world where nothing yet has a meaning but the loving care of her mommy and daddy. What many parents don't know is that babies have different crying. For every negative emotion that they experience, they use a different pitch sound to voice their complaints.

If your baby is crying, she is doing it for a reason. Most of the times, her reason is one or a combination of:

- She is hungry.
- She is uncomfortable.
- She is tired or sleepy.
- She is bored.
- She is sick.
- She disapproves of routine changes.
- She has colic.

The lamenting sounds will vary according to the cause. You will learn to distinguish between your baby's crying variations as you move forward. For the beginning, decipher the two most prevalent cries in babies:

- The fussy cry
- The protesting/angry cry

Let's break them down and see what makes them stand out!

The Fussy Cry

Babies get fussy when they are tired, bored, or uncomfortable. You will notice a whiny, nasal, continuous cry that builds in intensity from your baby when she needs sleep or when the surrounding environment is annoying. Babies may also become

fussy when they are sick. Here, you might hear a soft whimper in a lower pitch coming from your little one.

When you sense your baby is fussy, try to identify quickly what the cause is. Remove any annoying elements around her. Try feeding her and check if her diaper needs changing. She might just need a nap, but if your instinct tells you she's sick, contact your pediatrician.

The Protesting Cry

This form of crying is the next level of fussy crying. It occurred when you cannot soothe your baby in time, and now she is angry in her little way, and she makes sure you notice.

However, your baby may also use protesting cry to let you know she disapproves of the recent changes in her schedule. It often occurs when you are trying to implement a sleep training routine. Here, she will cry angrily between two to four nights into the following routine. From then on, she should accept the changes naturally.

Colic and the Witching Hour may also cause your baby to cry in protest for hours. You need to ensure that the baby is comfortable. Make sure the baby is fed, has a clean diaper, comfortable clothes, and temperature. Try touching or giving the baby a gentle massage. Mommy or daddy's touch to the baby is soothing and comforting. You can keep him busy or distracted by taking a walk around the neighborhood or backyard if the weather permits it. Sing while making eye contact to remind your baby that you care, stay calm, and portray confidence to bring a sense of peace.

For some parents, the protesting cry can be challenging to manage. Sometimes, the baby understands she can have her way simply by acting angry. So, she "blackmails" her parents with angry screams whenever she craves a bit of attention.

You can avoid this problematic behavior from your baby by not responding immediately to every unfounded angry cry that she makes.

This table will help you understand better the differences between fussy crying and protest crying.

Possible reasons	Fussy Crying	Protest Crying
Hunger	A low-pitched, repetitive cry	A high-pitched, rhythmic cry
Fatigue	A whiny, nasal, continuous cry	An intense, whining howl
Discomfort	A whiny cry with body movements	An intense cry, nearly screaming
Boredom	A low-pitched whimper	A high-pitched, non-rhythmic cry
Sickness	Soft, nasal whimpers	
Changes in her routine		Intense crying that gradually decreases to almost nothing
Colic		Intense wails or screams that go on for hours

REASONS WHY BABIES STRUGGLE TO SLEEP

Babies use their protesting cry to communicate. You notice your child will use it predominantly at bedtime if she is not well sleep trained. Sometimes, the lamentation will be so intense that both you and the baby will struggle to get a good night's rest. There are various reasons for your child's tantrum before sleep, and they include:

1. The baby is too tired.

Overtired babies have a more challenging time falling asleep and staying asleep. The causes for your little one being too tired may differ depending on her age, her health condition, and the recent changes in her sleep routine.

Signs of your baby being overtired include a cranky mood, having problems settling in the crib, and an outright meltdown. You can prevent this situation by following a consistent bedtime routine every night and the baby's wake time. Also, avoid over-stimulating your child before going to bed. Sometimes parents think that putting a baby to sleep late will help him sleep better, but unfortunately, the opposite is true. When you let a baby stay awake for too long beyond their age-appropriate wake time, they will have a hard time falling asleep soundly at night or even at nap time.

If your child is overtired, try one of the soothing methods such as the Five S's of baby soothing, The Hold method, sound machine, and ensure that the room temperature is between 68 to 72 degrees Fahrenheit. Darkness also helps in increasing sleep pressure and encourages a conducive quiet sleeping environment. Unfortunately, these techniques will only work with newborns up to three months old. In other cases, look for sleepy cues throughout the day, pay close attention to age-appropriate wake periods to ensure that the baby will not sleep too early or too late during the day. This can also make it hard to keep a balanced schedule that can disrupt the baby's internal clock, making it hard to fall asleep. Don't forget about activities, activities, and activities to burn some energy. Establish a solid bedtime routine, be consistent with it, move bedtime a bit earlier into the evening, and teach by example by portraying a confident, happy attitude.

2. The baby is not ready to sleep.

Some evenings, your baby might have a hard time going to sleep. Even if you follow each step in her bedtime routine, she remains with her eyes wide open, cooing and playing.

You know very well that if you delay sleep for too long, the baby might feel overtired the next day, and that will be an even bigger challenge for your mission to establish a healthy sleeping routine.

To solve the problem, create a cozy environment around your baby. Begin by making the room dark and quiet. Remove any elements that may stimulate her attention, like toys or electronics. Sing a lullaby and gently massage her on the tummy and, when she calms down, retreat her to the crib. In the short term, establish a bedtime routine that reminds the baby that the "night, night" time is approaching; that way, he is prepared and ready to sleep.

3. The baby is relying on sleep props.

Sleep props for babies are habits that you have instilled in them in the first months of life, consciously or not. They may include:

- Rocking to sleep
- Holding to sleep
- Nursing to sleep

If your baby needs you to be around and actively help him go to sleep, they have developed a bad bedtime habit. We know that any baby out there will be better off if he learns to fall asleep independently.

Fortunately, bad little habits like this one can easily be unlearned. You will need to read your baby's sleepy cues. Have an organized schedule, spend quality time with your baby for him not to "miss" you during sleep, check wake times, and encourage independent sleep by strategically putting him down to the crib while he is awake. For a newborn, you can let him become drowsy at first before placing him in the crib, then gradually put him to bed when he is more awake than the last time. Instead of rocking or holding your child to sleep, let him fall asleep on his own, and this way, you will be sure that he has an excellent sleeping foundation that he can carry on well into adulthood.

The first few nights of trying new sleeping habits are not always fun since your baby will feel that something is missing and voice his concern aloud. From fussy crying to screaming protests, you will hear them all depending on the baby's temperament. You will need to remain strong, remember your "why's," the main reasons you want to give the gift of sleep to your little bundle of joy, and repress the urge to soothe him at his first snivel to allow him to learn the precious skill of self-soothing. Eventually, your child will get used to the new bedtime routine and sleep with no props.

4. **The baby's sleep cycle is not mature yet.**

Babies are born with a different sleep-wake cycle than adults have. In the beginning, babies have a simpler and shorter cycle, which they gradually adapt to that of an adult within a few months of life.

You, as an adult, have a sleep cycle that includes several stages of deep sleep and REM or active sleep. Each cycle lasts for about ninety minutes. When one ends, you either wake up or begin a new cycle.

Newborns have a sleep cycle that lasts for about forty minutes. They are much lighter sleepers than adults, and they can wake up at the slightest sound they perceive. Suppose your newborn baby has problems falling asleep. In that case, it might also be because her sleep cycles have not matured yet, and she will mostly need help to fall asleep during these first three months of her life while her brain is developing to be mature enough to regulate sleep on its own. You will need to stay calm and carry on with the bedtime routine and put her in her crib when drowsy but awake. This is the only period you can allow sleep props such as rocking

20

or holding to sleep but as much as it may be hard, try to limit the sleep prop of nursing to sleep as it becomes tough to break off the habits once they get very used to it. You can always nurse your baby but make sure that you keep her awake throughout the whole feeding session to avoid feeding-sleep association. That can make your baby develop a habit of waking up looking to nurse even when they are not hungry, interrupting their sleep.

5. **Your baby is experiencing a growth spurt.**

A growth spurt is a period in the life of a baby when he grows faster than usual. During this time, your baby will be fussier. He will also want to eat more and sleep even less.

It is not an easy period, but remember that it is just as fleeting as any other stage in a child's early life. Your baby will take shorter naps and wake up more often for feeding at night. More so, he will refuse to go back to sleep once he's awake.

My advice is to make the best of this time. Feed your baby well to support the growth spurt. Stick to the usual bedtime routine and patiently wait for your infant's rebellious phase to pass. Ensure enough practice activities during the day, maintain the wake times, follow the schedule, routines as usual; if the baby is not sleeping but calm in the crib, just let him be. Quiet time can also be helpful as long as the baby is not crying and just hanging out in his crib. This may allow him to fall asleep since he is not being stimulated.

6. **Your baby is going through sleep regression.**

Sleep regression is a period when a baby suddenly has trouble sleeping. It usually lasts between two to six weeks, during which he will have trouble settling down or suddenly wake up unexpectedly at night, even when he was a sound sleeper before.

The sleep regression stage is natural, and it occurs when your baby reaches a new developmental milestone, like sitting, standing, or crawling, for example. Other factors like traveling or disruption in her routine may also trigger sleep regression.

While you cannot prevent sleep regression, you can still reduce the factors that exacerbate it. Try sticking to a strict bedtime routine and ensure he gets enough rest and plays throughout the day.

7. Your baby is teething.

Your baby's teeth will start coming out between three months and their first anniversary. Teething occurs differently in babies. Some may have no symptoms at all. Others will cry and have severe sleeping problems because of the pain they experience.

If your baby is within the teething age parameters, she might have trouble falling asleep or staying that way because of those tiny "pearls" coming out of her gums. Signs of teething include excessive drooling, biting, crying, and refusing to eat. You can ease teething pain and help your child get a good night's rest by giving her something to chew on. Babies like the counter-pressure that soft toys pose against their aching gums, and always contact your pediatrician when you are concerned about your baby's condition.

8. Your baby is adjusting to the time zone after a recent travel.

If you travel with your baby within his first year of life, you might have to deal with him having sleeping problems. Long-distance traveling may have a bigger impact on a baby's sleeping routine than it has on an adult's sleep schedule.

Your baby may have trouble falling asleep or resuming her rest after waking up suddenly, especially when she is adjusting to a new time zone. Some babies may become fussy even when you travel to the next town. It differs from one infant to another.

When this happens, your best choice is to make a sleeping environment as peaceful as possible and keep routines similar. Make the room dark, remove stimulating elements, perform your regular bedtime routine, keep things quiet around the room, and if possible, use the same crib bedsheets and sleep sack to make the baby as comfortable as possible. When you get back home, resume the regular eat-play-sleep.

9. **Your baby disapproves of the sleep environment.**

Sleep-trained babies can easily sleep anywhere and everywhere, safe, of course, without having to protest against it. They adapt quickly to new environments and are always happy to go to sleep. This does not happen just by surprise, though. It is because they have mastered the precious skill of self-soothing, but also they are more independent. They don't have to depend on sleep props or fall asleep in a particular area or situation. Many past clients send me pictures of their babies when they are away from home, and the baby is sleeping peacefully in a bright room and in a hotel crib, which is an unfamiliar environment for the baby, but with no protesting. Some send pictures of babies taking a nap at the beach (keeping in mind at the beach, it is bright and noisy, no need to depend on darkness or super quiet times, and the baby still figures out a way to fall asleep just like an adult would if they took a nap). But this training does not kick in on the first night for some older babies. Their habits are already set in, and they are likely to protest the changes with all efforts. We know babies dislike changes even though they are constantly growing and changing; it is essential to study their emotions and reactions. Some babies need a bit more time to adjust than others, so slowly and gradually move those changes for the more sensitive babies.

You can also solve this issue by testing different elements that make a sleeping environment perfect for a child. Try experimenting with the levels of light and darkness in the room at bedtime. Do the same for the level of sound and stimulation until your baby will fall asleep easily and with less crying. Check the baby's room temperature (68-72 degrees Fahrenheit). The crib should be empty to reduce distractions and, for safety, dress the baby in comfortable clothes, keep the room dark to encourage melatonin production, a critical hormone in healthy sleeping. Ensure that they have enough age-appropriate activities during the day, and these may be tummy time for the tiny ones, take a stroll to the park or around the block, let them play in the backyard, run around and allow them to explore, and so on. There is something magical about the outdoors that helps babies to be more ready for naps or bedtime.

10. Your baby doesn't like the recent changes in the sleep routine.

Frequent changes in bedtime routine can make your baby fussy and difficult to soothe throughout the day. Changes such as different times for going to sleep, different night feeding, irregular time for baths can overwhelm the baby and lead to intense crying and protesting. Giving the baby time to adjust and get used to the new habits will help the baby eventually understand the routine and get used to it. Having a consistent and predictable sleep routine will help the baby settle in quicker at night and go to sleep without feeling restless.

11. The baby is too cold or too hot.

The temperature in your room or the nursery plays a big part in your baby's rest. Abnormal temperatures may decrease sleep quality and make the baby feel uncomfortable. Unsurprisingly, being too hot or too cold will make your baby challenging to go down for bedtime.

Make sure that the temperature in your baby's room is easy to control. Install a thermostat for your heating system if possible; there are some baby monitors with a built-in temperature monitor and set the temperature between 68° and 72°F (20° to 22.2°C) for a peaceful good night's rest and dress the baby in weather clothing.

12. The baby is hungry.

Babies do not have many priorities, but hunger is undoubtedly at the top of their list and overrides sleep. So, when they feel their little stomachs rumbling, they will let you know through crying. Your child will not go to sleep until her tummy is full. So, whenever she feels fussy before bedtime, ensure that you fully fed her to avoid unnecessary tears.

13. The baby is lonely and/or bored.

It's not ideal for comforting your baby at the tiniest whine. This behavior will lead to her becoming exceedingly needy and almost impossible to leave alone or with other people. However, your child may sometimes feel lonely or bored right before bedtime. She will let you know through low whimpers she needs affection. Do not disrupt her sleepiness, try to rub her a bit on the belly, sing a lullaby, and generally reassure her of your love and care. Spend more time with her during the day and make her bedtime routine longer to have more time for bonding and affection.

14. The baby is extremely attached to mommy or daddy.

I mentioned earlier, becoming attached to you or your partner could backfire in the long run for your baby and you. And side effects include but not limited to him refusing to stay with babysitters, relatives, and friends. You may find it difficult to have some time for yourself and your needs.

Also, the baby's neediness could affect his sleep. He might require intense and prolonged help to sleep well into his childhood years, affecting his ability to be more independent.

Your best choice is to reduce your baby's clinginess gradually. Please do this by not jumping to soothe him whenever he cries for attention. Also, ask a relative or friend to stay with him for a few hours when he's awake to develop social bonds with others. Encourage independent play while working on your projects or doing different house chores; keep a watchful eye on the baby, but don't make it evident that you are watching so that he can feel more in control. This way, the baby will become more confident and begin exploring on his own, hence becoming less and less too attached to you.

15. The baby is experiencing separation anxiety.

As you try to make your baby less attached to you or your partner, he might experience separation anxiety. A feeling of abandonment may make him impossible to go to sleep or enjoy a good night's rest. Separation anxiety usually appears between the first eight and ten months of your baby's life. To reduce your child's fear of desertion, gradually increase the time you are away. Leave him with your partner and come back an hour later. Then, do the same, but now come back two or three hours later. This way, he will get used to you leaving but feel reassured about your return.

CHAPTER FIVE

Predictability: Establishing Predictable Habits

BABIES THRIVE WHEN THEY KNOW WHAT TO EXPECT

Imagine yourself reaching a foreign country where you do not know the language or the local customs. You cannot read the signs, and nothing looks like anything you have been used to all your life. Also, nobody understands what you're saying or what you want. It sounds like a stressful situation that would keep you in a constant state of anxiety, doesn't it? Well, this is how your baby is feeling in her first months of life.

Your baby feels love and affection in your smile and voice, even if she can't understand a word you are saying. She feels the comfort of your embrace and the warmth of your feeding bosom. So, emotionally, she experiences fulfillment. Even as an infant, she needs some predictability or something to make her feel comfortable and know what to expect. You would need it in the scenario above, even if you felt the kindness of strangers around you.

So, for your baby to thrive, you need to add a bit of structure into her life, and a bedtime routine is a perfect place to start. You are doing the same things every day before sleep to help her know what to expect and diminish her anxiety.

Her bedtime ritual may include feeding, a quick bath, massage, and entertainment as singing, reading, and quiet playing. Regardless of the order you choose for these actions or what actions you choose to incorporate in your daily routine, stick to it to understand what you want her to do next, which is to sleep.

The slightest changes might make her fussy. And her becoming moody is understandable. She now has to experience a new dimension of her existence, and the stress of going through something completely unknown could make her unhappy. Your best choice is to change her bedtime routine, but gradually.

Circadian Rhythms

A circadian rhythm is a natural, internal process that regulates the sleep-wake cycle. As adults, we already have a circadian rhythm established, which does not change much until we reach our retirement years. Babies, however, are yet to form a circadian rhythm within the first few weeks of life. For this reason, besides many others that we listed above, infants wake up frequently at night. Many times, they have trouble going back to sleep as well.

You can help your baby get her circadian rhythm in sync by giving her cues of the difference between daytime and nighttime.

Day and Night Confusion

During the day, you can make the room lighter, more stimulating, and be louder in your actions, whether you are singing, playing, or just talking to her. At night, do the opposite. Dim the lights in her room and whisper. Reduce playing time and make the sleep environment as less stimulating as possible.

Your baby should steadily adapt to a natural circadian rhythm and wake up less often at night.

Melatonin

Melatonin is a hormone primarily released in the body to regulate the sleep-wake cycle. It also helps regulate blood pressure and defends stress.

We produce this hormone from birth. For babies, the melatonin levels become regular in about the third month after birth, with the highest levels measured between midnight and 8:00 a.m. Our ability to produce melatonin decreases with age, which is why older people sleep less at night in their golden years.

After roughly twelve weeks from birth, your baby should start producing melatonin regularly. The hormone will help her build a healthy sleep-wake cycle and adapt easier to a bedtime routine. This natural occurrence is essential for when you start sleep training your baby.

However, in the first three months, your baby may have difficulty falling asleep at night. Her production of melatonin is irregular at this stage. As a result, you might often see her waking up at night randomly or being fussy before bedtime.

Fortunately, you can increase the natural production of melatonin in your baby through simple actions. Try giving her a gentle, soothing massage before bedtime. Not only will this help her relax and fall asleep quicker, but it will also help the two of you bond better.

Swaddling a newborn baby should also enhance her feelings of security, coziness, and comfort. For older babies, putting on a sleep sack will instill a luring invitation to sleep, and subsequently, to higher melatonin production.

Keeping the room quiet and at a moderate temperature should help your child develop the ability to produce melatonin regularly. Support your baby by not changing a bedtime routine too drastically or too often to avoid unnecessary sleep troubles.

Sleep Stages

Scientists have come up with five sleep stages based on our brains' behavioral characteristics when we sleep. Babies, like adults, go through each stage during their lengthy slumbers, which may amount to seventeen hours per day in their early months.

Here are the five stages of sleep that your baby experiences:

1. **REM Sleep**

Also known as Rapid-Eye Movement Sleep, this stage occurs shortly after falling asleep, and it is when dreams occur. If you observe your baby, you notice her eyes move rapidly back and forth underneath her eyelids. Usually, more than half of a baby's daily sleep takes place in the REM stage.

2. **Non-REM Sleep Stage 1**

During this stage, your infant will experience a light sleep, the kind you would go through when feeling exhausted.

3. **Non-REM Sleep Stage 2**

The baby will enter a deeper sleep now, from which she will be more difficult to wake. However, she may still react promptly to nearby sounds and movements.

4. **Non-REM Sleep Stage 3**

Your child reaches deep sleep, and she no longer moves or startles when she hears sounds or movements.

5. **Non-REM Sleep Stage 4**

This stage is of profound sleep, and the less likely to see your baby wake up at random sounds or movement around her.

Your child will go through all five stages of sleep repeatedly throughout her sleep. Sometimes, they may wake up right between passing from the fourth stage of non-REM sleep to REM sleep and might have trouble falling back to sleep again. Sleep training becomes essential to gently teach the baby to transition from one sleep cycle to another without disrupting their sleep.

Understanding Drowsiness but Awake

If you are a first-time parent, you will hear others with more experience than you talking about "drowsy but awake" when referring to baby sleep training. It may have a strange ring to it, but this technique is crucial in helping your child develop healthy sleeping habits that last a lifetime.

Drowsy but awake means putting your baby down to sleep before she leaps into closing her eyes and sleep. This practice will teach her how to fall asleep on her own. This way, she will not depend on your cuddles, a swing, or any other sleep-inducing gimmick to fall asleep.

Babies who always require help to fall asleep and wake up very often and have a hard time falling back to sleep on their own, and so they cry more in protesting for whichever way mom or dad used to fall asleep.

Here's how to put your baby down to sleep while he is still drowsy:

> - The evening routine may include bath time, quiet playtime, and turn off lights, putting baby in the crib while he is still awake. While playing with your baby, you will notice subtle cues of her drowsiness, such as yawning, rubbing her eyes and ears, and so on.

> - You might feel the need to comfort her with cuddles and swinging. Instead, do the opposite. Instead, put on her sleep sack, tell her your "night, night" phrase, then place her on her back in the crib while she is still awake, meaning her eyes are wide open and she is aware of her surroundings. Avoid waiting until she dozes off, as this means she is already in her first stage of sleep, and she will probably need to be put in that stage before going to sleep between sleep cycles.

> - You can start practicing this method of laying the baby down for sleep from the first weeks of life. Add it to your bedtime routine and maintain the consistency to help your child get used to sleeping alone.

Drowsy but awake may be more challenging to implement on infants who are overly attached to their parents. If that is your case, you should first try to create a bit of separation between you and your baby before trying this technique.

I. SIGNS THAT BABY IS NOT GETTING ENOUGH SLEEP OR IS READY TO SLEEP

I have already mentioned most of the causes that can make it difficult for your baby to fall asleep. In most situations, your child will suffer from sleep deprivation, and you do not want her to go through that sorrow because it will make life harder for both of you.

If your baby is not getting enough sleep, these are ten ways she'll let you know about it:

1. He cries more often.

Sleep deprivation is difficult. It makes your child feel tired all the time, but it increases stress and anxiety. As a result, the baby will cry more often and for no apparent reason. Every tiny thing may upset him, and he is less willing to socialize.

2. She turns her face away

Babies look away from any stimulants or persons, even their parents, when they want to soothe themselves to sleep. If your baby is fussy and turning her face from you often, it means that she isn't happy with the amount of sleep she's getting.

3. She brings her hands to her head.

When your baby is overtired, he will even try to caress himself to sleep. Touching his head and face is a sign that he wants to be soothed and go to sleep.

4. He is rubbing her eyes.

Getting too little sleep is like having a weight put on your eyelids. We sometimes get this heavy feeling as adults. Babies feel it even heavier, which is why they try to rub their eyes and ease the pain.

5. She is overly clingy.

If your baby is fussy and cries almost instantly after you leave her side, she might suffer from sleep deprivation. Lack of enough sleep makes her clingy, needy, and craving constant comfort and attention.

6. He is easily irritable.

Your baby may become cranky and difficult to please when he is not getting the rest he needs. Ironically, he might become easily irritable right before bedtime and refuse to go to sleep.

7. She is hyperactive

You know your baby's sleep habits are not in shape when she is too active right before going to bed at night. If you have changed her sleep schedule, she will move and talk to herself more intensely. You might think that she is well-rested and fully energized. However, you will be surprised to know that these signs point to her being too tired to go to sleep.

8. He becomes clumsy

Sleep deprivation hurts your baby's motor skills and reflex abilities. If he mindlessly knocks off toys or loses balance easily, it means that he needs a steadier bedtime routine that ensures he is getting a good night's rest every night.

9. She becomes fussy before feeding.

When they suffer from sleep deprivation, babies want nothing else to be relieved from the constant feeling of tiredness. Not even food will appeal to them, which is why your child may become fussy and refuse food even on scheduled meals.

10. He has a hard time waking up.

After losing the balance in his sleep schedule, your baby will do his best to recover all the lost rest on future slumbers. You may find it difficult to wake him up even after a long period of sleep, and when you finally manage it, he will be cranky and moody.

CHAPTER SIX

Safe Sleeping For Babies Guideline

For safe baby sleeping, there is one rule of thumb that every parent in the world should respect at all times. **Baby must always sleep alone, on her back, and in her crib.** Here's how it applies!

Alone

You should avoid the temptation of taking the baby into your bed at night. In her early years of life, she could easily suffocate if a pillow or a blanket would accidentally land over her face.

On Her Back

Never leave the baby sleeping on her tummy since it may increase the risk of Sudden Infant Death Syndrome (SIDS) in the first six months.

Even after this age, I always encourage parents to put the baby to sleep on her back even if she may later turn to her tummy.

In Her Crib

Your child shouldn't sleep in a different bed. Keep her in her bassinet or crib with no pillows or blankets that may pose a hazard at night.

Sleep Tips for Newborns

- ✓ Swaddle
- ✓ Use a white noise machine
- ✓ Follow an Eat-Wake-Sleep cycle
- ✓ Establish a gentle bedtime routine
- ✓ Pay close attention to wake periods
- ✓ Change diapers strategically (like after waking, before going to sleep, of course after a soiled or wet diaper, check the number of changes and how full they are to ensure that the baby is well hydrated and well-fed)
- ✓ Watch for signs of sleepiness
- ✓ Put baby to sleep drowsy but awake

Sleep Tips for Infants

- ✓ Pay attention to wake periods.
- ✓ Follow the Eat- Play- Sleep schedule.
- ✓ Activities, activities, and activities between naps to burn some of the energy.
- ✓ Create a consistent solid bedtime routine.
- ✓ Put baby to sleep calm, ready to sleep but fully AWAKE.
- ✓ Be patient and stick to your daily schedules and routines.

Sleep Tips for Toddlers

- ✓ Pay attention to wake periods.
- ✓ Establish a consistent and predictable routine
- ✓ Set a solid bedtime routine.
- ✓ More activities between naps to burn the energy

✓ Ok to use a security blankie or lovey for toddlers who may experience separation anxiety.

✓ Put baby to sleep calm, ready to sleep but fully AWAKE.

ENCOURAGING EYE CONTACT

We know eye contact is an excellent way to show confidence and engage in communication or activities. It is also a great way to boost independence besides other skills. Encourage eye contact with your baby to engage and develop his confidence during the day. Talk to him, be silly, make funny faces, respond to his gestures and minor sounds, carry out a "conversation" with him while looking straight into his eyes, and encourage him to look at your face straight into the eyes as well. He will be more curious, interested in his surroundings, and willing to explore more, developing independence.

At night or nap time, though, reduce the eye contact since the baby will think that it's time to play/engage, yet it is instead a quiet time for "night, night" time.

CHAPTER SEVEN

The Overall Baby's Temperament

We know we cannot change someone's personality or temperament, but there are many ways we can encourage a positive temperament. When a baby presents a specific behavior, what you do may positively or negatively impact other activities' reactions and become a norm.

When a child listens to daddy more than he listens to mommy or vice versa, there may be a component that makes him choose to do so. This can be how firm a parent is, how confident they sound, how encouraging or supportive a parent is, how tolerating, compromising a parent is, how they set boundaries in loving and positive manners and follow through. It could be their bond and what they do when they spend time together. I noticed this pattern in how sleep training can be affected by many of the traits mentioned above. When the baby does not take you seriously, it will be hard for him to listen to you. And listening plays a significant role in making a smooth transition during sleep training. For example, he will think that you are probably playing when you tell him it's "night, night" time since he has already put you in that zone that you simply do not follow through or mean what you said. When you tell a baby not to throw his food on the floor, and he keeps doing it happily (because he thinks you are playing) and you keep repeating the same thing over and over, he does not take you seriously. While I encourage you to be nice and reasonable all the time, there comes the time when you have to put on your "parent" outfit and help your child gently learn to obey mommy or daddy or also other caregivers. It's a skill that is needed early in a baby's learning ability and will help the child grow into a more responsible, understanding, and respectful little human being.

When you talk to your child, instead of giving orders, teach him why what he is doing is not how it's done and show him how it's done. For example, you can show him for the food example while using gestures it's yucky, or the floor becomes yucky when we throw food on the floor. It may sound funny to talk to a baby, but it will surprise you by how much they learn well and faster.

Looking frustrated only encourages undesired behavior. Babies are constantly learning about the cause and effect of things. The more you look frustrated or irritated by a certain behavior, the more the baby will want to see more of that reaction by repeating the behavior. Stay calm, take a deep breath if it's a bit too much for you and teach your child that what he is doing should be done this other way.

Avoid too many no's not to make it sound normal that you say no to everything. Pretend not to notice the less unwanted behavior, this way to discourage the baby from doing it again.

Reward the baby for a reasonable effort and exaggerate your happiness to encourage the desired behavior that way; he will want to see more of that happiness by not throwing food on the floor, for example.

When you give a warning, lower to the baby's height, look in his eye and with **a neutral but firm voice**, say, for example, "No more throwing food on the floor. It's very yucky!" He will probably notice that you are serious and stop the behavior.

If you ever give a warning with a consequence such as taking away the teddy bear if he keeps chewing on it, **be sure to follow through** immediately so that the baby can learn to listen to you. For example, if you first say, "We don't chew teddy bear. Chewing your teddy will give you "ouchie" in the tummy." If he does it again, lower to his height and say, "It's not nice to chew teddy bear!" If he does it again, you can take it away for a few minutes and tell him why you took it away to understand the reason for that consequence.

Listening helps to develop a stronger bond and trust between a parent and a child. When a child trusts you, he will be more willing to try new things that you show him. And so, listening and learning go together since helping your child to develop his listening ability will eventually make it easier for him to learn pretty much anything and hence more accessible to sleep train.

CHAPTER EIGHT

Things To Pay Attention To During Sleep Training

FROM FOUR MONTHS AND OLDER

WAKE TIMES

Despite its name, sleep training your baby starts with the wake period and not when she is asleep. To get the best out of this crucial period in your child's life, take complete control of her wake time or wake window. This is the length of time that the baby can tolerate to stay awake, and it goes according to the baby's age. It is vital to follow age-appropriate wake periods to reduce unnecessary tantrums when the baby is not ready for sleep or is overtired to sleep. With a bit of planning and persistence, you can help your baby develop healthy sleeping patterns for many years to come.

How much time does a baby need to sleep?

Many parents ask me this question. The amount of sleep babies need depends on their age. That amount differs from one baby to another and varies from month to month. However, the following chart will give you a better idea about how much time a baby should be awake according to age. Following recommended wake times with durations of sleep can make an enormous difference between a baby who fights bedtime and a baby ready to sleep. In between the wake time intervals, your baby will nap. The length of her wake periods, the number of naps, and their length differ slightly from one child to another. The variation will depend on mood, health condition, daily energy, food quality and quantity, and playtime duration.

AGE IN MONTHS	WAKE PERIODS	NAPS	MAX DAY SLEEP	TOTAL SLEEP DAY+NIGHT
1 MONTH	1 HOUR	4+ NAPS	5-6 HOURS	14-18 HOURS
2 MONTHS	1.25 HOURS	4+ NAPS	5 HOURS	14-17 HOURS
3 MONTHS	1.5 HOURS	4 NAPS	4 HOURS	14-17 HOURS
4 MONTHS	2 HOURS	3-4 NAPS	4 HOURS	12-15 HOURS
5 MONTHS	2.25 HOURS	3 NAPS	3.5 -4 HOURS	12-15 HOURS
6 MONTHS	2.5 HOURS	2-3 NAPS	3.5 HOURS	12-15 HOURS
7 MONTHS	2.75 HOURS	2-3 NAPS	3-3.5 HOURS	12-15 HOURS
8 MONTHS	3 HOURS	2-3 NAPS	3 HOURS	12-15 HOURS
9 MONTHS	3 to 3.5 HOURS	2 NAPS	3 HOURS	12-15 HOURS
10 MONTHS	3.5 - 4 HOURS	2 NAPS	2.5-3 HOURS	12-15 HOURS
11 MONTHS	4-5 HOURS	1-2 NAPS	2.5-3 HOURS	12-15 HOURS
12-18 MONTHS	4-6 HOURS	1-2 NAPS	2-3 HOURS	11-14 HOURS
18+ MONTHS	4-7 HOURS	1 NAP	3 HOURS	11-14 HOURS
24+ MONTHS	NO NAPS	NO NAPS	NO NAPS	11-14 HOURS

SCHEDULES

Devise a Daily Schedule and Stick to It!

During the first year of her life, your baby will go through various accommodation stages to the differences between day and night. She will change her sleeping and eating patterns roughly every few weeks. You will need to expect these changes and alter her daily schedule accordingly.

You should know ahead that your child will not take the new modifications in her bedtime routine. They may seem minor to you, but to her will appear abrupt and confusing. Remember, she is still adapting to a world that you are accustomed to. So, be patient and gentle.

Schedule Sample for 0-3-Months-Old Babies

It is almost impossible to set up a consistent schedule for your baby during her first month of life. However, from four weeks on, you will notice specific patterns in her eating and sleeping needs. From this age to almost three months, she will most likely be awake for no longer than one to two hours at a time and need to sleep about fourteen to seventeen hours in twenty-four hours.

A sample schedule for a two months old baby may look something like this:

- **7:00 a.m.** - Awake & hygiene (change diaper)
- **7:15 a.m.:** Feed
- **7:45 a.m.** - Play (Tummy time, reading, singing, etc.)
- **8:15 a.m.** - Short routine for nap time (close curtains, change a diaper, swaddle, turn on the sound machine, read a book or sing, say "night, night," and place in the crib drowsy but awake)
- **8:30 a.m.** - Nap #1
- **10:00 a.m.** - Awake & hygiene (change a diaper, clean baby face, hands, put on a clean onesie, etc.)
- **10:15 a.m.** - Feed

- **10:45 a.m.** - Play (Tummy time, stroller walk to the park or around the neighborhood, etc.)
- **11:15 a.m.** - Short routine for nap time (close curtains, change a diaper, swaddle, turn on the sound machine, read a book or sing, say "night, night," and place in the crib drowsy but awake)
- **11:30 a.m.** - Nap #2
- **1:00 p.m.** - Awake & hygiene (change diaper)
- **1:15 p.m.** - Feed
- **1:45 p.m.** - Play (Tummy time, black and white soft toys, stimulate motor skills, shake rattles, talk to baby, touch)
- **2:00 p.m.** - Short routine for nap time (close curtains, change a diaper, swaddle, turn on the sound machine, read a book or sing, say "night, night," and place in the crib drowsy but awake)
- **2:15 p.m.** - Nap #3
- **4:00 p.m.** - Wake & Hygiene (change diaper)
- **4:15 pm:** Feed
- **4:45 p.m.** - Play (Walk around the neighborhood in mommy or daddy's baby carrier, play with the parent who is not around often during the day, read)
- **5:00 p.m.** - Short routine for nap time (close curtains, change a diaper, swaddle, turn on the sound machine, read a book or sing, say "night, night," and place in the crib drowsy but awake)
- **5:15 p.m.** - Nap #4
- **6:45 p.m.** - Awake & hygiene (change diaper)
- **7:00 p.m.** - Feed
- **7:30 p.m.** - Play or catnap
- **8:00 p.m.** - Bedtime routine (Bath time, gentle baby massage, quiet around the house, dim lights in baby's nursery, read, sing, talk, big hugs)
- **8:30 p.m.** - Feed (Try to keep baby awake while feeding with gentle touches on the cheeks, little tickle on the toes or tell a brief story, burp during a feeding session, then resume feeding.)
- **8:50 p.m.** - Burp one more time, clean diaper if necessary, swaddle, turn on the sound machine, say "Night, night, I love you," place the baby in the crib drowsy but awake, lights off.
- **9:00 p.m.** - Bedtime

While the baby may wake up every two to four hours at night, you may start by establishing good sleeping habits by practicing placing her back in the crib while she is still awake. For example, after feeding and burping, instead of waiting for her to sleep in your arms, you may place her in the crib while she is still awake. Do not push it though, at this age, it is practiced, and the baby is the boss. Just follow her lead. If she accepts it, that's great, but if she refuses to fall asleep that way, pick her up, use your regular methods, and then try again later or another day. With zero to three months old babies, we are practicing good sleep habits, but since the baby is still young and still adjusting to the outside world, we do not start the actual sleep training until the baby crosses the three-month-old mark.

Schedule Sample for Three to Six-Months Old Babies

From around three to six months, your baby will follow a more predictable sleep schedule and may sleep through the night. A sample schedule of a six months old baby should look something like this:

- **7:00 a.m.** - Awake & hygiene (diaper change)
- **7:15 a.m.** - Feed
- **7:45 a.m.** - Play (More playing on the floor or mat, practice crawling by placing a toy in front of the baby and encourage him to get it, peekaboo, sitting, clapping hands, stacking blocks, baby legs bicycling)
- **9:00 a.m.** - Nap time routine (close curtains, dim lights, change a diaper, put on a sleep sack, sing the baby's favorite song like "twinkle, twinkle little star" to signal that night, night time is coming, the baby picks books to read, point at pictures, colors, animals, gradually reading in a calming voice)
- **9:25 a.m.** - Tell the baby "night, night... I love you," and place the baby in the crib while AWAKE.
- **9:30 a.m.** - Nap #1
- **11:00 a.m.** - Awake & hygiene (change diaper)
- **11:15 a.m.** Feed
- **11:45 a.m.** - Play (Outdoor playing, stroller walk to the park or around the neighborhood, play in the backyard)

- **1:00 p.m.** - Nap time routine (close curtains, dim lights, change a diaper, put on a sleep sack, sing baby's favorite song like "twinkle, twinkle little star" to signal that night, night time is coming, the baby picks books to read, read, point at pictures, colors, animals, gradually read in a calming voice)
- **1:25 p.m.** - Tell baby "night, night... I love you" and place baby in the crib while AWAKE.
- **1:30 p.m.** - Nap #2
- **3:00 p.m.** - Awake & hygiene (change diaper)
- **3:15 p.m.** - Feed
- **3:30 p.m.** - Play (More playing on the floor or mat, practice crawling by placing a toy in front of the baby and encourage him to get it, peekaboo, sitting, clapping hands, stacking blocks, baby legs bicycling.)
- **4:00 p.m.** - Cat Nap #3 (only thirty mins)
- **4:30 p.m.** - Awake and hygiene
- **4:45 p.m.** - Optional little healthy snack, stroller walk around the block, quiet play, relaxing activities
- **5:30 p.m.** - Dinner
- **6:00 p.m.** - Bath time and gentle massage
- **6:15 p.m.** - Milk
- **6:30 p.m.** - Bedtime routine (close curtains, dim lights to encourage relaxation, change a diaper if necessary, put on sleep sack, sing the baby's favorite song like *Twinkle, Twinkle Little Star* to signal that night, night time is coming, the baby picks books to read, mom or dad reads the books, point to the pictures, name them, name the colors, the animal names, and sounds, talk to the baby and allow her to talk back)
- **6:55 p.m.** - Tell your baby "night, night... I love you" and place your baby in the crib while AWAKE.
- **7:00 p.m.** - Bedtime

Schedule Sample for Six to Twelve-Months-Old Babies

A sample schedule for a twelve to fourteen months old baby may look something like this:

- **7: 00 a.m.** - Awake & hygiene (change diaper)
- **7:15 a.m.** - Milk
- **7:30 a.m.** - Play more floor activities, independent play, stacking blocks, practice walking, playing with different colorful toys, following balls

45

- **8:30 a.m.** - Breakfast
- **9:00 a.m.** - Play time, outdoor playing, stroller walk to the park
- **10:30 a.m.** - A healthy snack
- **10:45 a.m.** - Nap time routine (close curtains, dim lights, change a diaper, put on a sleep sack, sing baby's favorite song like "twinkle, twinkle little star" to signal that night, night time is coming, the baby picks books to read, point at pictures, colors, animals, gradually read in a calming voice)
- **11:00 a.m.** - Morning Nap (#1)
- **12:00 p.m.** - Awake & hygiene (change diaper)
- **12:15 p.m.** - Milk & lunch
- **12:45 p.m.** - Play time (outdoor playing, stroller walk, running errands)
- **2:30 p.m.** - A healthy snack
- **2:45 p.m.** - Nap time routine (close curtains, dim lights, change a diaper, put on a sleep sack, sing baby's favorite song like "twinkle, twinkle little star" to signal that night, night time is coming, the baby picks books to read, read, point at pictures, colors, animals, gradually read in a calming voice, place baby in the crib while AWAKE)
- **3:00 p.m.** - Afternoon nap (#2)
- **4:00 p.m.** - Awake & hygiene (change diaper)
- **4:15 p.m.** - A healthy snack
- **4:30 p.m.** - Play more floor activities, independent play, stacking blocks, practice walking, playing with different colorful toys, following balls.
- **5:30 p.m.** - Dinner
- **6:00 p.m.** - Bath time and gentle massage
- **6:15 p.m.** - Milk
- **6:30 p.m.** - Bedtime routine (close curtains, dim lights to encourage relaxation, change a diaper if necessary, put on sleep sack, sing baby's favorite song *Like Twinkle, Twinkle Little Star* to signal that night, night time is coming, the baby picks books to read, mom or dad read the books, point to the pictures, name them, name the colors, the animal names, and sounds, talk to the baby and allow her to talk back)

- **6:55 p.m.** - Tell your baby, "Night, night... I love you" and place your baby in the crib while AWAKE.
- **7:00 p.m.** - Bedtime

We do not set these schedule samples in stone and they should not be the only source of inspiration for devising a daily schedule that is tailor-cut to your baby. The important thing is to stick to your desired schedule and be consistent. Give it at least a whole week before changing. In most cases, babies fit into the scheduling plans after a few days of adaptation.

The Do's and Don'ts of Sleep Training Your Baby

The Do's:

1. **Do develop** a nighttime sleep schedule that works for you, your family, and your baby. Something that you believe your family can be able to follow every night. It doesn't have to be big, complicated activities. Choose something simple that you think you can do even when you are super exhausted.
2. **DO** ensure your baby is well-fed and takes necessary naps during the day—good daytime sleep transitions to a good night's sleep.
3. **DO** develop a nighttime routine that is soothing and invokes sleepiness.
4. **DO** make sure you are prepared to follow through with your plan and give it at least a week of consistency before changing it.
5. **DO** be gentle and patient with your baby and never take it personally when you think the baby is not catching up. Every baby is different, and all they need is to feel comfortable. Changes do not feel fun for them, and they make it complicated by protesting so that you can give up and keep the old habits.

The Don'ts:

1. **DON'T** keep your baby up later at night to make him more tired.
2. **DON'T** begin sleep training until your baby is at least three months old.
3. **DON'T** send mixed messages or be inconsistent in your approach.
4. **DON'T** let your baby's sleep environment work against all of your efforts.
5. **DON'T** start it without help and agreeing with your partner and other household members.

The Benefits of Easy Daily Planning

When you start sleep training your baby, stick to a routine that is easy to follow. You cannot go wrong with using the eat-play-sleep pattern. It is the most popular cycle among parents worldwide, and it keeps both you and your child happy.

Your baby can quickly follow these three easy sequences:

1. She wakes up and eats. Feeling full makes her happy and gives you peace of mind.
2. After the meal, you play, sing, and cuddle. She feels entertained and loved, and you feel the bliss of seeing your baby grow and learn from one day to the next.
3. Once playtime is over, she steadily falls into a sweet and comforting slumber.

As your baby follows her daily scheduled naps, she gets the much-needed energy to grow and develop healthily. In the meantime, you get the benefits of having time for yourself and your home, which include:

- You can prepare a good meal.
- You can fold the laundry.
- You can spruce up your home a bit.
- You can order groceries or food delivery.
- You can spend some quality time with your partner.
- You can get in touch with your friends and family.
- You can get a bit of work done or prepare how to resume your career later.
- You can enjoy watching a series or listening to music, quietly, of course.
- You can practice your favorite hobbies like reading, gardening, or creating art.
- You can take a quick nap as well.

Sleep training should make your parenting experience much easier and more pleasant. You do not have to put your entire life on hold after you give birth. With proper planning, you can enjoy most of the things you used to do before pregnancy without affecting the happiness or health of your baby, your partner, or your other children.

CONDUCIVE SLEEP ENVIRONMENT

Very few babies slide into a sleep training schedule smoothly. Most infants protest against it for a few days but stay strong and focus on that light at the end of the tunnel. The long-term benefits outweigh the short-term discomfort. You have complete control over the situation, and you can also make the process easier and more pleasant by creating a conducive sleep environment.
Here are the elements you will need to control and ensure they help produce optimal sleep ambiance for your baby!

1. Temperature

Some parents make the mistake of overheating the room where the baby sleeps because they fear that the baby might catch a cold. Unfortunately, a too-hot room will make the baby sweat excessively, wake up repeatedly, and become fussy easily. Your best choice is to keep the warmth in the room at a pleasant, mild level. Maintain a constant temperature in the nursery between 68-72 degrees at all times. This way, your child will enjoy a sweet and peaceful slumber without waking up too often.

2. Light

Our brains produce melatonin, a hormone primarily released by the pineal gland that regulates the sleep-wake cycle. We produce it from birth, but infants only start enjoying its benefits after the first three months of their lives. To help your baby get enough rest and quality sleep, help her increase sleep pressure both at night and during her daytime naps. So, make her room as dark as possible. Even the slightest light can inhibit the production of melatonin. Use blinds, black-out curtains, or heavy curtains to block off any light coming from outside.

3. Distractions

Many parents fill the nursery with countless toys and balloons even before the baby is born. The enthusiasm is understandable. However, all those plush toys and dolls are highly stimulating objects for babies, preventing them from falling asleep easily.

Make sure that you remove all distractions from the nursery. And when your child can follow a sleep-wake schedule easily, then you can add a lovey or blankie. Until then, keep the stimulants in the room to a minimum.

4. Clothing

Babies sleep best in a soft cotton swaddle, especially in their first few months of life. However, as they grow older, they move more during their slumbers, so more appropriate clothing to their needs will do.

You want your baby to sleep comfortably, without feeling too warm or too cold, and to sway to her arms self-soothing when she needs it.

On warm nights, keep it light and breezy. A basic short-sleeve cotton bodysuit or T-shirt with a muslin or cotton swaddle on top is fine. On wintry nights, a pair of snuggly pajamas or a sleeping sack over standard cotton pajamas should do the trick.

5. The ABC Rule

The American Academy of Pediatrics strongly recommends that your infant should sleep ALONE on her BACK, and in the CRIB during her first year of life. This way, the risk of Sudden Infant Death Syndrome (SIDS) is minimal.

Your baby may roll over on her stomach alone during sleep, especially during her early infant months. At that point, it should not be a problem. However, while she is still under one-year-old, you should not sleep with your baby in the same bed or allow her to sleep with any other things in her crib.

6. Noise

Babies are susceptible to sounds in their early months of life. Remember that they have just entered an entirely new world, which differs from the setting they were used to in their mothers' wombs.

The baby can adapt to sleeping in a loud environment. But like adults, if the noise is not moderate and is disruptive, try to limit the noise in your household and ask everyone to comply so that your baby's sleep training will proceed easily. If your baby has problems falling asleep every night because of the slightest sounds around her, try using a white noise machine to balance the sound waves in her sleeping environment.

7. No Toys in the Crib

Except for a small lovey, there should be nothing else in the crib when your baby goes to sleep. Even the toys that have been specifically designed for infants can pose hazard risks. Plush toys, plastic dolls, and many more can cause choking or asphyxiation.

Also, keeping the toys in another place will help your baby distinguish between the play area and the bedtime area. This way, she can fall asleep with no distractions or confusion.

8. Smoke

Keep the baby's sleep environment smoke-free. If someone in your household has a smoking habit, ask them kindly to practice it outside as far as possible from the nursery. Tobacco smoke can damage the air quality in your baby's room drastically. If you spend the rest of your time in a smoking area, change your clothes and wash your skin before entering the house. This way, you will avoid making the air unpleasant and unsafe around the baby.

9. No cords

Whether you use a white noise device or a lamp in the nursery, keep them far from the baby's crib. Babies do not have complete control over their hands. They can easily reach and grab whatever is around them.

Suppose a lamp is on the side of their crib; your baby can pull the cord, causing it to fall into the crib. The risk of accidental self-harm and injury is increased by having anything with cords around the crib.

10. Picture Frames

Avoid putting any big or heavy picture frames in or around the baby's bassinet or crib. These objects have pointy corners and sharp edges that can severely injure them when you least expect them. They may accidentally fall, and you don't want them to fall in the crib when the baby is sleeping. You should keep the sleep environment as clean and clutter-free as possible to enhance your baby's sleep quality and health.

11. Fresh air

Sometimes babies' noses quickly get stuffy and congested. It is essential to keep the baby's room air fresh, free from powerful scents either from perfumes or scented cleaning supplies. The air should be clean at all times. Empty and clean your baby's diaper pail constantly to avoid soiled diaper smell from leaking and polluting the baby's room. Some baby-friendly odor removers may be placed in the diaper pail or move the diaper pail outside of the baby's room. High-quality air purifiers are also a great idea to put in the baby's room to remove air pollutants and keep the baby's nursery fresh and clean. You should always consult your baby's pediatrician or a qualified pediatric professional when buying something you are not familiar with to ensure that it is baby safe and helpful.

BEDTIME ROUTINE

If you feel the pressure of planning a bedtime routine for your baby, simply remember that you are following one, too. Most probably, every night before going to bed, you brush your teeth, wash your face, change into your pajamas, and maybe even read a bit before turning off the light. Your baby needs this kind of consistency, as well. Since she cannot do it herself, help her follow a smooth and predictable path to sleep every evening.

When to Start A Bedtime Routine

It's never too early to start a bedtime routine. However, the first few weeks of your baby's life are not suitable for implementing a bedtime routine yet. During this period, the baby is barely adapting to the new world. Your child first needs to discover the differences between day and night, the sounds and movements around her.

Around six to eight weeks is a suitable time for considering a bedtime routine. At first, keep it short and simple. You can start by reading from a storybook before sleep, singing, a little sponge bath or regular bath for older babies, or cuddling. Do not pressure yourself to come up with a complex routine that might stress the baby. Let it flow naturally as long as you can recreate the same experience every day.

How a Bedtime Routine Helps

A bedtime routine tells your baby that it is time to transition from the active and playful daytime to the coziness and tranquility of nighttime. And so, the routine should calm and relaxing.

When you are consistent with your baby's bedtime routine, you provide her with comfort and predictability. She counts on you for them when tiredness gets the best of her.
Having a good bedtime routine helps your baby go faster over the sleep regression period.

Finally, a proper bedtime routine helps you and other household members relax and follow your daily schedule without too many interruptions.

When Should the Baby Go to Sleep?

Bedtime differs from one stage of development to another during the baby's first year. As a newborn, your child will most likely go to bed around 9:00 p.m. As she grows older (four months and up), bedtime should start between 6:30 and 8:00 p.m., preferably at 7:00 p.m. It's essential to ensure that the last afternoon nap is not too close to bedtime to avoid difficulty falling asleep at bedtime. You will play a crucial role in defining bedtime. To establish a proper bedtime routine and maintain it with consistency, you may keep a log of your baby's sleeping patterns to monitor sleep habits, adjust wake times, and schedule accordingly.

Babies from four months old and above can sleep through the night, so they can sleep a stretch of ten to twelve hours per night.

The following table contains the recommended amount of sleep per night per age (0-36 months) should help you with devising a stable and predictable bedtime routine:

Age range	Recommended Hours of Sleep per Night	Recommended Hours of Sleep per Day
0-3 months old	8 to 9	5 to 8
4-11 months old	10 to 12	4 to 5
12-24 months old	10 to 12	2 to 3
24-36 months old	10 to 12	2

Three Examples of an Effective Bedtime Routine

You can start building a bedtime routine for your baby from scratch. However, if you are looking for a bit of inspiration, these three examples of tried and tested bedtime routines should come in handy:

1. **The natural way**

This routine should work on most babies out there. I'm calling it the "natural way" because many parents out there put it into practice without even acknowledging it. For them, it just comes naturally, and so it should do for you. It goes something like this:

- With about one hour before sleep, change her diaper, and give your child a nice warm bath.
- Make the last feeding of the day a gentle one filled with loving cuddles paying close attention to sleep cues. Avoid letting baby fall asleep in your arms as this can steal from the regular night sleep and end up making it difficult to fall asleep when you place him in the crib.
- Help your baby settle down by reading a book in a soothing voice with occasional eye contact.
- Talk to him in a calm, soothing, happy voice before placing him in the crib, but this time make sure that you place him in the crib while he is awake.
- Leave the room without looking behind to avoid unnecessary crying. When you look behind, the baby will probably see your face and feel the need to call you one more time. With this, he may start crying for you to come back. When you leave without looking behind, the baby

notices that you expect her to sleep, and it's now time to sleep, not to play.
- Turn off the lights off.

2. The Quiet Way

With this routine, you use minimal energy, and your baby goes softly to sleep with no unnecessary stimulations:

- Change her diaper, give her a comforting bath, and apply a baby-friendly lotion to moisturize her delicate skin (always check with your pediatrician for a baby safe moisturizer recommendation).
- Feed her (for babies four to six months old only) while in a dim, not too bright, quiet room.
- Give your baby a nice, comforting massage to calm her down.
- Read books with a calming voice, put on a sleep sack, say a key phrase to remind her it's bedtime, such as "night, night.. (baby's name), I love you."
- Place her in the crib while AWAKE and leave the room
- Turn the lights off

The Playful Way

This routine is perfect for babies who cannot get enough of playing and giggling. You don't want to make the bedtime routine boring, so here are a few ways in which you can make it fun without over-stimulating your child:

- After eating, play with your baby, and try to drain the last drops of energy without over-tiring him.
- Offer a long comforting bath to play with warm water, bubbles, and toys in the warm bathtub under your close supervision, of course.
- Sing a lullaby or a soft song for a more calming but entertaining effect in a dim light nursery.
- Read books, ask the baby to choose his favorite, and encourage him to name or find the characters or images in the book.
- Turn on the sound machine, tell night, night to things in the room (for example, good night windows, good night curtains, the good night dresser, good night books, and bookshelves)
- Put on a sleep sack, tell him a key phrase always to remind him that this is time to go to sleep such as "it's night, night - I love you ... (baby's

name)" sometimes if he is still talking you may say "hush, hush, it's night, night time" while putting your index finger on your mouth to signal "hush" then say "I love you (baby's name)"

- Put him into the crib while he is still awake and step away to let him fall asleep independently.

Important Bedtime Routine Tip

Regardless of the bedtime routine you choose, try to practice it consistently not to confuse your baby. To make it even more effective, divide the routine steps between you and your partner.

Although it sounds like a good idea to have both mommy and daddy in the nursery for the bedtime routine, it can be too exciting for the baby, and it may make it even harder for her to fall asleep. Your best choice is to have one parent do the bath and the feeding and the other take over quiet playing, reading, or singing until the end of the bedtime routine.

INDEPENDENT SLEEP/ SELF-SOOTHING

Trying to make a routine bedtime work for your baby requires control, persistence, and flexibility. There will be nights when your little bundle of joy will fall asleep immediately after the bath or after feeding. While it may feel tempting to leave it there and call it a night, do your best to keep your baby awake for the duration of the routine to reach, for example, the 7 pm bedtime. If he keeps becoming too sleepy before the actual bedtime, adjust the bedtime routine duration to a shorter period close to the set bedtime. For example, in this situation, you may start a bedtime routine at 6:45 p.m. instead of 6:30 p.m. to avoid the child from falling asleep ahead of the desired time.

Encourage independent sleep!

Avoid rocking and or holding your baby to put him to sleep. Refrain from doing anything that you don't want to repeat in the middle of the night if the baby wakes up. You don't want to be rocking baby for forty-five minutes at night because that's what you do at bedtime. Try not to help the baby reach the first stage of Non-REM sleep, which is when the child's eyes are heavy, closes them to doze a bit and opens them, and so on. Doing so will teach him that to fall asleep, mommy or daddy will help me reach my first sleep stage.

To be sure that someone has mastered what you taught them, you let them do it without you intervening, right? And I believe this is the best approach to everything for learning. Instead of you helping your child to tie his shoes all the time and he will need you every time he wants to go outside to play in the backyard, for example, you instead teach him how to tie the shoes on his own so that he does not have to depend on you whenever he wants to play in the backyard. That translates to him being independent and boosting his confidence to do and learn more things on his own!

Whatever method you use at bedtime, the baby will claim the same method in the middle of the night to go back to sleep. It's better to help him learn how to fall asleep independently so that if he wakes up between sleep cycles, he can go back to sleep on his own without disrupting his sleep as well as yours.

When Should I Put My Baby Down When She's Drowsy but Awake?

Taking advantage of your baby's drowsiness is part of helping her develop healthy sleeping patterns. You can implement it from a young age and as early as six weeks. Make it a regular part of your evening schedule to be on the lookout for your baby's cues of drowsiness.

Remember that your baby may not always agree to be left alone when she is drowsy. In the beginning, she might release a few cries of protest and soft whimpers. You should try to delay responding immediately and instead let her find her way to sleep. It will benefit the baby more in the long-term than always jumping in at every moment you hear her sound, which robs her of the precious opportunity of learning how to self-soothe and fall asleep independently.

How Do I Put My Baby Down Awake?

You can easily learn how to put your baby to sleep by studying her sleep patterns and tiredness cues. Here are a few things you can try:

1. Look out for her sleep clues.

Train your eye to notice the earliest signs of tiredness in your baby, such as yawning, eye rubbing, and even a bit of fussiness.

2. Wake times and Schedules

Pay close attention to the baby's age-appropriate wake windows. These will help you ensure the baby is not overtired or less ready to sleep. Schedules go hand in hand with wake windows as they balance the Eat-Play-Sleep patterns.

3. Stick to the bedtime routine.

If you have already settled on a bedtime routine, stick to it and apply it, whether it's time for nighttime sleep or a daytime nap.

4. Try to separate eating from sleeping.

Make feeding the first part of her bedtime routine, just after the bath and before playtime starts. This way, she will not fall asleep at the bottle or the breast and will not associate feeding with sleeping.

5. Do not enter the room at the first whimper.

If your baby cries at night, do not enter the room immediately. Wait for a few minutes and allow her to fall back to sleep by herself as long as you know she is OK, safe, and not sick.

Age (in months)	Delay before feeding at night (minutes)
0-2	2-3
3-4	15
5+	20-25

6. Keep your visits to the nursery short.

If you have to enter the nursery at night, make sure that you don't linger there for too long not to stimulate her and end up waking her up. Go in, give her some quick comfort by patting her on her head or rubbing her tummy, and get out. Try not to pick her up. You want to signal to her it is still nighttime and that she has to go back to sleep.

7. Keep the nursery room conducive to sleep.

Remember to keep the room dark to encourage the baby's internal clock to realize that it's sleepy time. Keep the room at a comfortable temperature (68* to 72* F) for a simple transition to dreamland. Don't forget the sound machine to block out all the unwanted noise from outside and encourage a more continuous sleep.

What If "Going to Bed Awake" Doesn't Work?

We know babies do not react well to changes in their bedtime routine, no matter how small they are. They fear change at first because they do not know if it's good for them or not.

It would come as a huge surprise if the "Going to bed awake" technique worked from the first time you use it. For most parents, it doesn't, and it's normal. We are working with tiny human beings, and so they have their ways of responding to changes. The only way to have success with it is to practice it consistently. You may use gentle approaches to help him learn to fall asleep on his own gradually, and with consistency, babies adapt pretty quickly.

Once they learn to soothe themselves to sleep, they will go along with your decision and not require your help or reassurance.

However, if your baby is reluctant to learn how to fall asleep on her own, you can try these simple tips:

- Eliminate sleep props from the nursery.
- Gradually reduce too much attachment if she is becoming too clingy.
- When playing, choose fun activities to do together that consume her energy but also for bonding.
- Go on a stroll around the neighborhood, and the fresh air should help her sleep better when you get back home.
- Take her to new places like parks, music classes, and other entertaining locations.

As with any new skill, practice makes perfect for sleep training your baby. Maintain the consistency for as long as you can. Sleep training is like a giant puzzle; it will not be complete if one piece is missing. It's essential to follow the above tips to see positive results.
If that fails, pause it and do it at another time when you feel more comfortable to resume the training again.

Milestones by Age 0 - 36 Months

All babies develop on their terms and timelines, which do not differ as much as you would expect. By the time your baby turns three years old, she should have a complete set of teeth, walk, communicate her needs and wants, play, and even feed herself.

Where Does Sleep Training Fall in All of This, And How Does It Count?

Besides teaching your child how to walk, talk, and sing, showing her how to fall asleep on her own will help her develop a lifelong skill that will nurture her health and make learning the other aspects of life much smoother for decades to come.

Sleep training helps build healthy sleep patterns that your baby can carry with her long into her adult years. It can also help her sleep with very few or no interruptions and no need for comfort in the middle of the night. Not only does she benefit from it, but everyone in the household will enjoy peaceful slumbers, as well.

Developing a healthy sleep pattern will help your baby thrive, improve her brain activity, and give her more control over her motor skills in the first months of life.

Here is a breakdown of the main milestones in your baby's development within her first three years and how sleep training plays a part in it!

0 - 3 Months

Your baby's first three months of life won't bring you too many changes in her behavior. She will sleep, eat, and cry most of the time as she gets used to the world and the surrounding people. Toward the end of this period, she might make her first sounds other than whimpers and cries and even give you her first smile.

Motor Milestones

- While lying on her tummy, she pushes up on arms.
- While lying on her tummy, she lifts and holds her head up.
- Able to move fists from closed to open.
- Able to bring hands to mouth.
- Moves legs and arms off of the surface when excited.

Sensory Milestones

- While lying on the back, she attempts to reach for a toy held above her chest.
- While lying on the back, she visually tracks a moving toy from side to side.
- While lying on the back, she keeps her head centered on watching faces or toys.

61

- Able to calm with rocking, touching, and gentle sounds.

Communication Milestones

- Quiets or smiles in response to sound or voice.
- Turns head toward the sound or voice.
- Shows interest in faces.
- Makes eye contact.
- Cries differently for different needs (e.g., hungry vs. tired).
- Coos and smiles.

Feeding Milestones

- Latches onto nipple or bottle.
- Her tongue moves forward and back to suck.
- Drinks 2 oz. to 6 oz. of liquid per feeding, six times per day (since babies are different, always consult your pediatrician for your baby's feeding needs).
- Sucks and swallows well during feeding.

You cannot impose an efficient sleep training method in the first three months of the baby's life since she is still adjusting to her new world and her sleep cycles are not yet mature. Instead, this is the time to establish good sleep habits (simple bedtime and nap time routines, sleeping in her crib), so by the time the sleep cycles and her brain are more mature, she will have a great foundation. Babies at this age will sleep around fourteen to seventeen hours per day in short stretches. All you need to do is learn her tiredness cues, follow the ABCs of safe sleeping, swaddle, and comfort her with love, care, and affection.

3 - 6 Months

During this period, things become more exciting for both you and your child. The baby understands her environment, and she differentiates between the people who visit her. Since her brain and sleep cycles are more mature, this is a time to begin sleep training and to establish a solid bedtime routine with daily rituals like bathing, playing, singing, or reading from a book.

Motor Milestones

- Uses hands to support her while sitting.
- Rolls from back to tummy and tummy to back.
- While standing with support, she accepts the entire weight with her legs.
- Reaches for nearby toys while on her tummy.
- While lying on the back, she reaches both hands to play with her feet.
- While lying on the back, she transfers a toy from one hand to the other.

Sensory Milestones

- Uses both hands to explore toys.
- Happy when not hungry or tired.
- Brings hands and objects to mouth.
- Able to calm with rocking, touching, and gentle sounds.
- Is not upset by everyday sounds.
- Enjoys a variety of movements.

Communication Milestones

- Reacts to sudden noises or sounds.
- Listens and responds when spoken to.
- Uses consonant sounds in babbling, e.g., "Da, da, da."
- Makes different sounds to express feelings.
- She notices toys that make sounds.
- Uses babbling to get attention.

Feeding Milestones

- Shows interest in food.
- She opens her mouth as the spoon approaches.
- Moves pureed food from the front of the mouth to back.
- Eats cereals and pureed foods–smooth, pureed food (single ingredient only), like carrots, sweet potato, squash, apples, pears. (Always follow your pediatrician feeding recommendations specific to your child.)

The main problems that may interfere with sleep training during this period include teething, sleep regression, colds, and illnesses. Navigate around them and try not to pause or stop sleep training unless her health condition prevents you from continuing the daily bedtime schedules and routines.

Remember that sleep regression is natural and that it will frequently occur in your baby's first year of life. Even if she is losing the progress that she made so far, continue to reach the sleep training goals you have set in the beginning, not to lose track, and have to start over again.

Six to Nine Months

This period in your baby's life is exciting and crucial in her development. She can now move by herself when sitting, lying down, or crawling. She can also attempt to communicate. However, the biggest progress is in her wake time.

Now, she can be more active between the naps. She is more responsive to games, toys, singing, and to you reading from a book. Your baby should feel more comfortable adapting to changes in her bedtime routine despite sleep regression.

Motor Milestones

- Sits without support.
- Sits and reaches for toys without falling.
- Moves from tummy or back into sitting.
- Moves with alternate leg and arm movement, e.g., creeping, crawling.
- Picks up head and pushes through elbows during tummy time.
- Turns head to track objects while sitting visually.
- Shows more control while rolling and sitting.
- Picks up small objects with thumbs and fingers.
- In simple play, imitates others.

Sensory Milestones

- Enjoys a variety of movements, bouncing up and down, rocking back and forth.
- Explores and examines an object using both hands and mouth.
- Turns several pages of a chunky (board) book at once.
- Experiments with the amount of force needed to pick up different objects.
- Focuses on objects near and far.
- Investigates shapes, sizes, and textures of toys and surroundings.

- Observes the environment from various positions while lying on their back or tummy, sitting, crawling, and standing with help.

Communication Milestones

- Uses an increased variety of sounds and syllable combinations in babbling.
- Looks at familiar objects and people when named.
- Recognizes the sound of her name.
- Takes part in two-way communication.
- Follows some typical commands when paired with gestures.
- Shows recognition of commonly used words.
- Simple gestures, e.g., shaking head for "no."
- Imitates sounds.

Feeding Milestones

- In a highchair, she holds and drinks from a bottle.
- Eats thicker pureed and mashed table foods.
- Enjoys chewing toys that can massage sore and swollen gums during teething.
- Stays full longer after eating.
- Looks and reaches for objects, such as food that is nearby.
- Shows a strong reaction to unfamiliar smells and tastes. (As always, remember to follow your pediatrician recommendations for food and feedings since babies have different feeding needs.)

Sleep regression is again a significant factor influencing sleep training at this stage. It is ideal to perfect the "drowsy, but awake" technique to the "is going to sleep AWAKE" technique. If you have been practicing it for months, your baby should be able to fall asleep on her own.

The development in communication and the addition of thicker foods to her diet will increase her excitement. Unfortunately, being more anxious than usual about separation and attachment issues will also affect her sleep quality.

Nine to Twelve Months

Every parent out there remembers this exciting period in their child's development. It is the stage in your baby's life when she makes her steps and possibly says her first words. Playtime is more fun and versatile at this stage, helping you be more flexible with her bedtime and pre-nap routines.

It is the time when your baby requires attention and unlimited engagement. She can sleep for longer stretches both throughout the day and night. Therefore, you have more time for yourself and get to sleep better and for longer stretches, too.

Motor Milestones

- Pulls to stand and cruises along with the furniture.
- Stands alone and takes several independent steps.
- Moves in and out of various positions to explore the environment and get desired toys.
- Maintains balance in sitting when throwing objects.
- Claps her hands.
- Releases objects into a container with a large opening.
- Uses the thumb and pointer finger to pick up tiny objects.

Sensory Milestones

- Enjoys listening to songs.
- Explores toys with fingers and mouths.
- Crawls to or away from objects that she sees in the distance.

Communication Milestones

- Meaningfully uses "mama" or "dada."
- Responds to simple directions, e.g., "Come here."
- Produces long strings of gibberish in social communication.
- Says one or two words.
- Imitates speech sounds.
- Babbling has sounds and rhythms of speech.
- Pays attention to where you are looking and pointing.
- Responds to "no."
- Begins using hand movements to communicate wants and needs, e.g., reaches to be picked up.

Feeding Milestones

- Finger feeds self.
- Eating an increasing variety of food.
- Uses an open cup.
- Ready to try soft-cooked vegetables, soft fruits, and finger foods (banana slices, cooked pasta).
- Might be ready to start self-feeding with utensils.
- Enjoys a greater variety of smells and tastes. (Check with your pediatrician about your baby's food and feeding needs.)

Baby sleep training should come easy at this stage. Though bad sleep habits are already set in, you may notice intense protesting to go back to old habits since babies are this age are strong-willed, and they want things to go their way. A temporary return of sleep regression and intense teething pain may disrupt your schedule for a bit, but it should not take away from your child's progress.

Twelve to Eighteen Months

Your baby has just celebrated her first anniversary. She has already experienced the Daylight Saving Times (DST) confusion and most of the new events in her first year. By now, feel more comfortable in sleep training your baby because it is also easier to communicate with her.

Babies pass from two naps per day to a long one during this time. Usually, it is the morning nap that goes away. Instead, the toddler has more time, patience, and energy to play. You will find it easier to travel with her without disturbing your sleep training schedule too much.

Motor Milestones

- She walks independently.
- Squats to pick up a toy.
- Stacks objects.

Sensory Milestones

- Helps with getting dressed /undressed.
- Has a regular sleep schedule.
- Eats an increasing variety of foods.

Communication Milestones

- May use five to ten words.
- Combines sounds and gestures.
- Imitates simple words and actions.
- Consistently follows simple directions.
- Shows interest in pictures.
- Can identify some body parts when named.
- Understands fifty words.
- Responds to questions.
- Repeats words overheard in conversation.
- Continues to produce speech-like babbling.
- Points at familiar objects and people in pictures.
- Understands "in" and "on."
- Responds to yes/no questions with a head shake/nod.

Feeding Milestones

- Increases the variety of coarsely chopped table foods. (Check with your pediatrician for your baby's specific food and feeding need.)
- Holds and drinks from a cup.

Even if your baby might seem that she masters a sleep routine at this stage, still try your best to teach her healthy sleep habits. Sleep regression may still occur, and separation anxiety could still affect the quality of her sleep.

Your best choice is to maintain a strict bedtime routine even if you have to shorten the duration of some rituals like bathing, singing, and quiet playing before bed.

Eighteen to Twenty-Four Months

From eighteen months to two years old, your toddler should find sleep training easier to cope with, as she will get between eleven and fourteen hours of sleep per day. Sleep regression related to separation anxiety,

68

nightmares, and fear of the dark may still occur, so it is vital to stick to or introduce good sleep habits.

Communication Milestones

- Uses at least 50 words.
- Consistently imitates new words.
- Names, objects and pictures.
- Understands simple pronouns (me, you, my).
- Identifies more body parts when named.
- Understands new words quickly.
- Uses few-word phrases.
- Uses simple pronouns (me, you, my).
- Understands action words.
- Uses gestures and words during pretend play.
- Follows two-step related directions, e.g., "Pick up your coat and bring it to me."
- Enjoys listening to stories.

Twenty-four to Thirty Months

At this age, your child has a great deal of energy. Wear her off through playtime and learning activities before naps and nighttime slumber. However, pay attention not to over tire her, which will have the opposite effect and make her feel too tired to go to sleep.

Also, from this age, she might not want to sleep in her crib anymore. While the risk of Sudden Infant Death Syndrome (SIDS) is not present anymore, and you could have her sleeping in the same bed with you, it's always better and good practice for her to sleep in a single cot or her bed alone. This controls too much attachment, separation anxiety and helps her become more independent since she doesn't have to depend on mommy or daddy being in bed to fall asleep.

Communication Milestones

- Consistently uses two to three-word phrases.

- Uses "in" and "on" in her sentences.
- The caregiver understands at least 50% of speech.
- Follows unrelated two-step directions, e.g., "give me the ball and go get your coat."
- Understands basic nouns and pronouns.
- Understands "mine" and "yours."

Thirty to Thirty-Six Months

As she reaches her third birthday, your child will be comfortable falling to sleep independently and following the bedtime routine that you have established and adjusted since she was an infant.

Communication Milestones

- Asks "what" and "where" questions.
- Uses plurals, e.g., "dogs."
- The caregiver understands most speech.
- A simple understanding of concepts including colors, space, time.
- Understands "why" questions.
- Understands the simplest sentences.

Now is the ideal time to give your baby choices regarding the rituals in her bedtime schedule. She can have her pick from singing, playing, activities, or reading from a book. Giving your toddler some choices in her bedtime routine may help her feel more in control and avoid tantrums. Try letting her choose which bedtime story she wants to hear or which pajamas she'd like to wear. The trick is to offer only two or three options, each of which you're happy with regardless of her choice.

At this age, she will only need one nap during the daytime, and she will need between twelve and fourteen hours of slumber per day. The only thing that could disturb her sleep is the occasional nightmare. When this happens, you can enter her room and comfort her. You may also use rewards such as "if you go to sleep now, we will go to the beach tomorrow, or you will get "favorite" stickers."

CHAPTER NINE

During Sleep Training

YOUR MINDSET & READINESS

- Emotionally stable
- Ready to follow through
- Give it a week of consistency before changing a method

Be mentally ready to sleep train and determined to follow the process and set at least two to three days dedicated to sleep train, and I recommend that the non-nursing parent be the one to put baby to sleep for the first three days. This makes it easier as the baby doesn't associate nursing with sleeping, reducing the tears. And studies have shown that fathers' involvement in bedtime routine leads to too few night awakenings.

For Babies Four Months and Older

Start on a Friday evening or on days you have free schedules such as on a weekend or your days off to give you ample time to adjust to recent changes.

Avoid these sleep training obstacles:

- Inconsistency
- Pacifier dependency
- Lingering or staying for too long in the bedroom which only upsets the baby and prevents him from learning to self soothe
- No drowsiness (The baby must be fully awake during bedtime and nap time routine, not even slight sleepiness.)
- Not following the plan in total will make it hard to see full results
- Night one is about change, have patience
- Night two can be the hardest, more patience and stay focused on your main why's (goals) and at that light at the end of the tunnel
- Night three progress sinks in, stay consistent with the plan
- Night five is fighting back for the last time so that it can be a tough one. Don't give in! The baby is doing his best to go back to old habits, and he will voice it harder than before. Stay strong and stick to the plan.

CHECKLIST BEFORE SLEEP TRAINING

Checklist:

- ✓ Both parents agree.
- ✓ Family members agree with the plan.
- ✓ No screen time before bed.
- ✓ Aim for at least one hour between eating dinner and bedtime.
- ✓ No toys in the crib.
- ✓ Room completely dark.
- ✓ White noise machine and a baby monitor camera.
- ✓ NO pacifier.
- ✓ Bedtime routine thirty mins before set bedtime.
- ✓ No less than three to three and a half hours of awake period between last nap and bedtime.
- ✓ Bedtime between 6:30-8:00 p.m.
- ✓ Falls asleep within ten mins of going to bed.

✓ Night sleep should be between ten to twelve hours of night sleep.
✓ No rocking or other sleep props to sleep.
✓ Bath time.
✓ Sleep sack.
✓ At least two favorite books.

Pay Close Attention to These Ten Points During Sleep Training

Wake period or wake times, or wake windows are the periods between the moment babies first awake (open their eyes after sleeping) to when they fall asleep again (they close their eyes again). We know babies are different, but this is one thing they have in common according to their age. Like adults, sleep is even more important in young children's daily life to grow and thrive mentally, emotionally, and physically. They have a specific range of time they can handle to stay awake healthily. If they go beyond that time, they are overtired. If they go to bed earlier than that wake window, they are not ready to sleep, and they will fight against sleep. So, it is critical to get their sleep timing right to avoid unnecessary intense tears. A baby ready to sleep is more cooperating, less fussy, less cranky, and quickly winds down and falls asleep.

Feedings - Keep them hydrated, avoid feeding association by keeping feedings out of the nursery and avoid feedings with the sole purpose of getting the baby to fall asleep. Your child should be done with all feedings thirty mins before bedtime for food to digest to avoid spitting up. Avoid constant snacking not to teach the baby that the only way for him to stop crying is with nursing or feeding. Ensure that the baby is fully fed so that he does not have to wake up because he is hungry. Always talk to your pediatrician when you have specific feeding or food issues. Usually, babies from four months and older can sleep through the night but since all babies are different, please first check with your doctor to recommend appropriately according to the baby's growth, health status and health history, weight, and so on.

Sleep Environment - Temperature (68 - 72* F), complete darkness, free of distractions, comfortable clothing, safe ABC sleep (Alone, on their Back, and in the Crib) it's ok if they roll over on their stomach on their own. Free of noise, conducive to sleep, no toys in the crib, except a lovey or blankie, no cords, away from smoke, avoid placing heavy picture frames close to the crib.

Bedtime Routine - Calming activities to get baby ready to sleep; bedtime should be between 6:30 p.m. and 8 p.m. Choose a routine to follow as presented earlier. Follow the **Feed+Routine+Bedtime Formula** and take turns for a bedtime routine. Though it sounds like a good idea to have both mommy and daddy in the nursery for the bedtime routine, it can be too exciting for the baby, making him fight sleep. Have one parent maybe do feeding, bath time, and pajama dressing, then the other parent to take over and carry on the routine until bedtime.

Activities, Activities, and Activities - Ensure that your baby has enough activities to burn energy. Take a walk or stroll around the neighborhood, go to the park, attend music class, baby rhymes, play in the backyard, read books, sing and make funny sounds (It's incredible how babies love melodic sounds). Talk to them, engage with them with eye contact, have them touch and feel soft objects, encourage them to repeat simple words, tummy time for little ones, practice crawling, standing or walking, and so on.

Sleeping Independently/Self-soothing - Put baby to bed awake by eliminating sleep props. Break the "too much attachment" issue by spending more time with the baby during the day and gently giving him space to explore and play independently. Offer comfort, but don't let the baby fall asleep while you provide that comfort.

> **Sound machine:** Helps block out unwanted noise, help baby stay calm, and sleep better. Ensure that the sound

machine has baby-friendly lower decibels, and monotonous sound is better to avoid sleep disruption when the baby is transitioning from one sleep cycle to another.

Baby monitor: Ensure that you can see the baby through a video baby monitor to ensure that he is safe.

Consistency: Don't give up; it only makes it worse. Changing too many things often confuses the baby and makes it difficult to understand what you want the baby to do, know or recognize. Choose a method and stick to it; give it at least a week to sink in before moving to another. Babies thrive when they know what to be expected.

Patience (Parents): Stay calm, show baby you are confident then they will become more confident, be sweet but firm in your voice for baby to know that you mean it when you tell him to go to "night, night." Envision your goals; you would like your baby to enjoy a well-rested sleep, to enjoy all the benefits of a well-rested baby, and for you to get more done whether it's fixing a healthy meal, catching up with friends, doing that yoga class or simply relaxing on the couch with your partner, so that when you feel like giving up, let those be your motivation and remember that you are giving your child a precious gift of sleep that they will probably carry well into adulthood.

CHAPTER TEN

Sleep Training Strategies

Quick Checks but Not in A Whimper (Confidence-Boosting)

- When you go in, avoid eye contact. We know eye contact usually is a good thing because it shows that we want to engage with the other person, but in this situation, we do not intend to engage the baby to chat or play with us; it is time to sleep. So, it's for that reason we avoid making the baby play instead of focusing on going to sleep. Say, "I love you, baby, it's night, night time," and leave their room without looking back even if you hear tears behind you.

Give Yourself A Set Time That You Are Comfortable to Check on Him and Stick to It.

- Have a watch or timer. One minute can feel like ten hours for a parent who is hearing a crying baby. Choose no less than five mins (ten mins), though, since too little time will feel like a game to the baby, and he may continue to protest as he knows you will be back in a few seconds. This is also to give him a chance to figure out how to fall asleep by himself and giving him a chance to express his emotions.

Avoid Picking Up

- Many babies become more upset when you pick them up and then put them back into the crib; it is also a way to avoid creating another sleep prop of the baby feeling the need for mommy or daddy to hold him before they can fall asleep. We are trying to eliminate anything that can create another sleep trouble if it is not offered.

Stick to five mins for three checks and only stay inside the room for one minute

- You may tap on his butt (babies love it) or gently rub on his back or sing. He will probably be upset but keep your voice neutral, smiling a bit, to bring in the sense of security and for the baby to see that he has nothing to worry about.

Don't Show Your Baby That You Are Nervous Or Don't Know What To Do.

Remember that however a mom or dad reacts, the baby feels it and reacts accordingly.

Agree with People in the House.

My husband can't handle hearing a baby crying, even on the street. When he hears a baby cry, it visibly bothers him, so at our son's four-month sleep regressions, he suddenly started waking up at night crying. My husband could not help waiting for the five-minute check period; any parent can tell you that even one minute of a baby crying can feel like an eternity or like ten hours of crying. So, whenever he was about to give in and go check on him after just a few seconds, I would tell him, "Honey, I love you, but you know that if you go in after just a few seconds, he will make it a habit and you will have to go in tomorrow and so on." So be mentally ready to sleep train and be determined to follow through with your plan.

Sleep is essential for everyone since it helps to restore our body energy. It also helps in muscle growth, tissue repair, protein synthesis, and growth hormone release. A baby who does not sleep well is cranky, tired, and has difficulty practicing milestones.

Our main goal for this sleep training is to ensure that your baby goes to sleep independently and teach or train him to soothe himself so that he can stay asleep longer, and when he wakes up between sleep cycles, he can be able to soothe himself back to sleep.

- ✓ Check and adjust your baby's awake periods, daytime schedules, appropriate nap length and number of naps, and the total amount of hours that he should sleep in twenty-four hours.
- ✓ Check, adjust, and correct bedtime routines, baby bedroom/nursery, nighttime waking, and early waking.

When habits are set in, and he is now aware of his regular habits, he will not be happy to see changes. This mainly results in intense crying and protesting. We will use gentle methods to reduce the crying though many babies may reject comforting. This is when it is crucial to be consistent and stick to the plan. Crying is a baby's way to express that he is not happy with the changes; it should not be confused with fear of abandonment. Once babies notice that mommy or daddy will not be giving in anymore, they adjust pretty quickly. The protesting cry usually stops within three to four nights for gentle but firmer methods, while for no tears methods, which are very gentle ways to wean baby off sleep props, it can take up to six months to see results.

Work on Teaching the Baby to Sleep Independently.

For a baby who requires help to fall asleep, when they wake up between sleep cycles (a sleep cycle is about thirty to forty-five mins long), they find it hard to fall asleep hence crying and requiring parents to repeat the same sleep prop used to put him to sleep at bedtime. For example, if the baby went to sleep while nursing, he would need nursing to go back to sleep. By teaching your child to self-soothe, we are sure that if he wakes up in the middle of the night or of nap time, he will put himself back to sleep requiring none of the previous sleep props or calling out for her.

Laying Baby to Sleep Drowsy but Awake.

When putting your child to sleep, it is imperative to put him in his crib when he is still awake. Drowsy means that he is ready to go to sleep, but he is still aware of his surroundings. This means that both of his eyes are open, and the baby must be awake. This can be tricky, but what we are avoiding is to lay baby down in his crib when he is already in his light sleep (in light sleep, the baby is dozing off; he has heavy eyes, and they are closing in and out). We want to make sure he is fully awake but calm and ready to go to sleep.

- ☐ Your baby should always sleep in his crib in his room at nap time and bedtime.

- ☐ Nursing/Feeding should be outside the baby's room to avoid sleep association and it should not end a bedtime or his nap time routine.

- ☐ Using appropriate schedules and wake time: The baby's schedule must be appropriate for his age. This is to ensure that baby is not overtired or not ready to sleep because of inadequate scheduling. It is essential to be mindful of the baby's awake period according to age; this way, the baby is ready to sleep.

- ☐ Don't rush in as long as you can visualize the baby and know that he is safe, sound, and not sick. You should wait for a couple of minutes before checking on him. This allows the baby to self-soothe. Going in right away robs the baby of the opportunity to learn the precious skill of soothing himself.

- ☐ Avoid giving in! Babies notice things pretty quickly, and they may notice that if they do something or continue to be fussy, mommy or daddy will give in since they gave in before. This will only make the situation worse. You may have to start over again. It is essential to stick to the plan and remember that you have chosen well by doing what is best for your baby. Though most babies at this age can sleep through the night (twelve hours), some may still need a feeding depending on their growth, weight, and so on. For that reason, I recommend checking with your doctor if you are not sure if you should feed your baby during the night.

Some babies may wake up during the night because they are genuinely hungry, while others may wake up because they are used to nursing to fall back to sleep, thus forming a habit of requiring the feeding as comfort, not because they needed it. Check the table below to differentiate a comfort feeding from a hungry feeding. Please note that this is just a guide. Since every baby is different, please check with your pediatrician to confirm your baby's feeding at night.

Differentiating a Hunger Feeding vs a Comfort Feeding

HUNGRY FEEDING	COMFORT FEEDING
The baby wakes up towards early morning after sleeping for most of the night	The baby wakes up frequently at night
The baby drinks most of the milk and stays awake through out the feeding	The baby drinks a very small quantity and falls back to sleep shortly after the feeding
The baby is laid into crib wide awake and falls asleep on his own	The baby cries when laid into the crib awake and requires to fall asleep first and while feeding before being laid into the crib

Recap

➤ Our principal goal is to teach your baby to sleep independently without relying on sleep props to fall asleep.

➤ Self-soothing is very important in learning how to transition from one sleep cycle to another. This also helps him to sleep longer and to stay asleep.

➤ Consistency is essential in helping your baby to know what to expect and when to expect it.

➤ It is also essential to stick to the plan and avoid giving in, as this creates setbacks that may lead to starting over again. A vigorous bedtime routine, appropriate daytime schedule, and mindful wake time will yield faster results.

➤ Crying is the baby's way of expressing that he is not happy with the changes and should not be confused with fear or abandonment though we should never let a baby cry it out. Remember that you are doing what is best for your child. Stick to the plan, it will soon pay off.

➤ Please contact the baby's pediatrician for the night feeding if you are not sure if you should feed him at night.

CHAPTER ELEVEN

Bedtime Strategy

LAYING BABY TO SLEEP DROWSY BUT AWAKE

When putting your baby to sleep, it is essential to put him in his crib when he is still awake. Drowsy means that he is ready to go to sleep, but he is still aware of his surroundings. This means that both of his eyes are open, and the baby must be awake. This can be tricky, but what we are avoiding is to lay the baby down in his crib when he is already in his light sleep (in light sleep, the baby is dozing off; he has heavy eyes, and they are closing in and out). We want to make sure he is fully awake but calm and ready to go to sleep. He will probably cry once you put him in his crib awake.

Below are the steps to fix this:

There are two different but tricky cries we are looking out for when a baby cries.

Is it a **"fussy" cry** or **"upset" cry?**

If the cry is a fussy, do not go in as long as you know he is safe and not sick. For this cry, he will cry for like one minute, then stop for another, and so on. He may quickly put himself to sleep. The baby is simply calling for attention. The cry is usually not loud, and it includes breaks. If you let him, he may fall asleep.

But if the cry becomes a real protesting/upset cry, then you can start checking on your watch for the time interval before you check on him. An "upset" cry is loud, continuous, and does not stop. It is the cry that feels like the baby will not stop crying, and it feels like he wants to get out immediately. For one minute of a crying baby can feel like an hour for a parent; having a watch around or something to keep track of the time helps with the quick checks. When a baby's habits are already set in, he will probably reject comforting. We will use a firmer method with quick checks as this method usually yields results within three to four nights.

Below are the steps to follow:

1. Have your watch and choose a time interval that you would like to check on him. Since it takes three to five minutes for the baby to be fully awake, I recommend choosing the time you are more comfortable waiting for, but the baby may turn it into a game if you go in too soon. Pick a time that is no less than 5 minutes and stick to that time. Wait for that time before checking on the baby.

2. Once the time is up, go in for one minute, check that everything is ok; you may gently rub on his back if he allows it; if not, talk to him with a calm, firm, and confident voice and no eye contact during the quick checks to avoid more tears. (If he uses pacifiers, check if the pacifiers are within his reach in the crib but do not insert them for him) then tell him a keyword such as "George, it's sleepy time," then leave the room without looking back.

3. He may cry immediately again. Wait for the time interval that you set before you go in. Repeat Step 2. This is to help him learn to go to sleep independently. The cry is a protesting cry to communicate to you he is not happy with the changes. You should

not feel you are abandoning him when you are checking on him more frequently. You just have to be consistent with the plan to teach him to soothe himself. This is the part you need to be patient and remember why you are doing this. It is for the best of your baby.

4.   Repeat step 2 until he falls asleep.

CHAPTER TWELVE

Night Wakings Strategy

WHEN BABY WAKES UP IN THE MIDDLE OF THE NIGHT

Since some babies may still need feeding during the night, please check with your child's pediatrician about night feedings and follow the doctor's instructions. If the baby still has a feeding, please ensure that you keep him awake by touching his toes, running your finger gently on his cheek, or saying something just for him to stay awake during the feeding. Once he has finished and ready for bed, tell him the keyword like, "George, it's sleepy time," then lay him in the crib awake, and leave the room.

For non-feeding waking, follow the steps below:

1. If the baby wakes up crying a fussy cry, let him be. He may put himself back to sleep. Going in too soon may rob him of the time to learn to soothe himself. As long as you can see him and know that he is ok, safe, and not sick, give him a few minutes to self-

settle. He may calm down and slowly fall back to sleep on his own.

2. If the cry turns into a real protesting/upset cry: Then wait for the same time interval you used during bedtime. Once the time is up, check and make sure that the baby is ok and safe. Make sure that the pacifiers are within his reach but do not insert it for him. Tell him the keyword "George, it's sleepy time." Help him to lie down if he is sitting up or standing. Then leave the room.

3. If he cries again, wait for the time interval again and repeat Step 2.

4. Repeat Step 2 until baby falls asleep. Please remember to be consistent and to stick to the plan.

EARLY WAKINGS STRATEGY

☐ Treat an early waking like a middle of the night waking.

☐ The best time to wake up for a baby is between 6-8 am.

☐ We are aiming for at least ten hours of straight sleep at night.

☐ If the baby wakes up after sleeping for ten hours, repeat Step 2 of the night waking, but try it for about twenty minutes. If he cannot go back to sleep, the sleep pressure may be low, and he may be ready to wake up.

☐ Sleep pressure is the urge we feel when we want to sleep. It is the lowest in the morning after a long stretch of sleep and is heavier in the evening when we feel ready to sleep. To discourage him from waking up early, start with a boring activity for him. He is not excited about changing his diaper, changing his clothes, and so on. Giving him something he is excited about only encourages him to wake up since he knows he will immediately start nursing or playing.

If he wakes up early but happy, do this:

- ☐ Use blackout curtain to block out 100% of the light.

- ☐ Limiting naps may help (more in the nap section below).

- ☐ Moving bedtime later may help. .Adjust the entire day schedule by moving up fifteen minutes each day until you have reached the desired bedtime routine. (For example, if you would like him to wake up an hour later, it will require four days to reach an hour later for bedtime.)

- ☐ And if he is talking to himself or calm, just let him be. This is good for him to learn that it is not yet time to wake up, making him fall back to sleep.

If he wakes up cranky and tired:

- ☐ He has most likely not slept up to ten hours.

- ☐ He may be overtired.

To fix this:

- ☐ Be mindful of the wake time according to the baby's age. An overtired baby may find it hard to sleep well.

- ☐ Don't allow the first nap too early since he woke up too early. He may get tired earlier and want to take a nap. Be mindful of wake time at all times to avoid the early morning nap to affect the rest of the daily schedule..

- ☐ Have a solid bedtime routine, quiet time, and low lighting before bedtime.

- ☐ Ensure that the room is completely dark and that the baby is not cold, hot, or wet.

☐ If you think the baby is hungry, use your judgment since you know your baby best. And follow your pediatrician's instructions on his early morning feedings.

NAP TIME STRATEGY

☐ Naps usually take much longer to see results than night waking. Most often, it may take two weeks, but sometimes it may take up to six weeks to see results.

☐ It is essential to be mindful of the wake time according to your baby's age group.

☐ Babies sleep better and longer at night when they have fewer naps.

☐ Naps extend the total sleep hours that a baby needs in twenty-four hours. If a baby's total recommended sleeping hours are twelve to fifteen hours in twenty-four hours, and he sleeps eleven hours at night, naps will be needed to complete the required twelve to fifteen hours of sleep that the baby needs in twenty-four hours.

☐ Put into consideration your baby's early morning waking and his age group. He may be ready to transition to two naps.

☐ A baby's nap should not stretch over three hours.

☐ When he wakes up early in the morning, follow wake time before putting him down to nap again. It is essential to stay consistent with the plan.

☐ Treat nap time waking as night time waking but limit the time that you spend trying for him to fall asleep. So, if the baby wakes up before one hour, treat it as the night waking.

Nap Training

☐ Set a short nap time routine such as in the following order: changing diaper, closing blackout curtains, turning on a noise machine, and reading a book. This is to quickly replicate the bedtime routine and prepare the baby that sleeping time is approaching.

☐ Tell your baby the keyword "George, it's sleepy time."

☐ Then lay him in the crib awake and leave the room.

☐ Use Step 2 of night waking. If he cries a fussy cry, let him be, but if the cry turns into a real protesting/upset cry, wait for the time interval, check if he is ok and that nothing is wrong, then tell him the keyword "George, it's sleepy time," then leave the room without looking back.

☐ Repeat Step 2 until he falls asleep.

☐ If, after one hour, the baby is still refusing to sleep, take him out for a twenty to thirty-minute break. (This is not one hour of a baby crying. It is one hour of trying to get the baby to sleep on his own). During this break, ensure that any activities you do are quiet or uninteresting, such as changing a diaper, and you may feed him outside his bedroom if feeding is due.

☐ Then try to put him back to sleep again for another hour.

☐ Though, rarely, he won't sleep for the second time, if he cannot sleep for the second hour, use a different sleep prop as long as it is not the one you usually use. For example, you can use patting on his butt while he is still in the crib if he allows you to. But you cannot rock, swing, sway, or insert a pacifier if your baby is already used to those.

☐ If you are not comfortable trying for two hours, use any other props that he is not used to after the one hour of trying. Back rubs involve rubbing the baby's back to calm him down, and once he calms down, you stop to help him learn to sleep independently. If he cries again, repeat the back rubbing, ensuring that you stop when he stops crying. Repeat until he falls asleep. If you choose to use this method, stop rubbing his back when he is a little more awake than last time until he will go to sleep independently.

☐ Nap training requires patient, sticking to the plan, and staying consistent.

SHORT NAPS

Brief naps are any naps that last less than one hour. They are primarily due to sleep props, milestones, or nap transition that a baby finds it hard to transition from one sleep cycle to another without help.

Short naps resulting from a nap transition will show a baby waking early in the morning, and the baby will flat out refuse to take his nap or is more challenging to put to sleep.

To fix this:

Start by increasing the awake time to the appropriate awake period and adjusting bedtime to the desired time.

Short naps due to sleep training: If the baby is sleeping through the night and then starts catnapping, he is now more rested and needs some time to adjust to the new sleeping stretches. This is normal, and it should improve.

To fix this:

☐ If a nap is less than one hour, treat it like a middle of the night waking and use Step 2 of nighttime waking. If he cries a fussy cry, let him be, but if the cry turns into a real protesting/upset cry, wait for the time interval, check if he is ok and that nothing is wrong, then tell him the keyword "George, it's sleepy time," then leave the room.

☐ Limit it to twenty to twenty-five minutes of trying. If he does not fall asleep after twenty to twenty-five mins, pick him up and continue your day.

- ☐ If he falls asleep, make sure not to go over two to four hours of napping according to his age.

- ☐ If he ends up taking another catnap, it's ok. Don't have him go back to sleep again as this may disrupt the rest of his daytime schedules, including bedtime.

CHAPTER THIRTEEN

Schedules Strategies

The baby's schedule must be appropriate for his age. This ensures that the baby is not overtired or not ready to sleep because of inadequate scheduling.

- ☐ If the baby sleeps ten hours per night, he should be ready for the day.
- ☐ If he wakes up earlier than ten hours, treat it like a nighttime waking but limit the time of trying to put him back to sleep to twenty minutes to extend the morning wake-up time (check the night-waking section). If he doesn't go back to sleep, take him out and get ready to start the day, making sure that the first activities are not exciting so that he does not form a habit of waking up while looking forward to it. Making it a boring activity to discourage the baby from feeling the need to wake up.
- ☐ Keeping the awake period consistent is important in sleep training since using appropriate wake time allows your baby's body to adjust when putting the baby to sleep. This also ensures that

the baby is not overtired or not ready to sleep, and it sets the right balance to the baby's entire day schedule.

☐ Diaper change in the middle of the night or during nap time should be avoided unless the baby is agitated and prevents him from going back to sleep. Some babies poop when sleeping, and they may wake up crying. If this happens, wait for a few minutes to give the baby a chance to self-settle before going in unless if the baby also has diaper rashes, then you will need to go in faster. You may also apply a significant portion of baby-friendly rash creams but, consult your pediatrician for your baby's appropriate recommendation.

RECAP

➤ Our primary goal is to teach your baby to sleep independently without relying on sleep props for them to fall asleep easily and quickly.

➤ Self-soothing is very important in learning how to transition from one sleep cycle to another, which helps him sleep longer and stay asleep.

➤ Consistency is essential in helping your baby to know what to expect and when to expect it. It is also essential to stick to the plan and avoid giving in, as this creates setbacks that may lead to starting over again.

➤ A strong bedtime routine, appropriate daytime schedule, and mindful wake time will yield faster results.

➤ Crying is the baby's way of expressing that he is not happy with the changes and should not be confused with fear or abandonment though we should never let the baby cry it out.

➤ Remember that you are doing what is best for your child; stick to the plan, it will soon pay off.

➤ Please contact the baby's pediatrician for the night feeding if you are not sure if you should feed him at night.

CHAPTER FOURTEEN

Obstacles That May Disrupt Sleep Training

Sleep training your baby may seem like a good idea to you, but it may not convince other household members. Despite being a scientifically proven technique for helping babies develop healthy sleep patterns, other people in your house may not agree with it. Your relatives and even your partner may find it difficult to accept it.

DEALING WITH HOUSEHOLD MEMBERS WHO DISAGREE

Fortunately, there are ways to deal with household members who disagree with sleep training, and the best way is through conversation, trial, and proof of results. If you have to convince your partner or other adults in your household, first, you do your research and come up with a list of evidence that supports your decision. That list can include all or any of the proven results below:

☐ Sleep training your baby does not have adverse effects. Other people may look at sleep training and think that it will damage the baby's health. They may even see it in practice and mistake the baby's cries of protest for pain or discomfort. Sleep training your baby does not have any side effects or negative conse-quences for the baby. She may cry a bit initially because changes in her routine usually confuse her, but once she gets used to them, having a predictable bedtime routine calms her down. And you don't have to let your baby cry for hours to see results. Though prolonged crying does not affect a baby health-wise, I am not a fan of letting a baby cry for a long time. You may use gentle ways to instill love and affection and still see positive results with min-imal tears.

☐ Sleep training your baby improves the parents' mood. Sleep training only takes a few days for both the baby and the parents to adapt to it. Afterward, everyone in the household can quickly adapt their schedules to the baby's bedtime routine and reap the benefits that come with it. This practice helps the mother enjoy her time while the baby sleeps and take care of household chores. It also helps her get a good rest, conserve her energy, and subse-quently improve her mood. Eventually, everyone in the family enjoys a stress-free, happy, calm, and stable environment.

☐ Sleep training has significant long-term benefits. If sleep training weren't beneficial for the baby, pediatricians would not recom-mend it. However, doctors worldwide consider it an effective way of improving your child's sleep, health, and ability to get a good rest for the rest of her life. Sleep training improves child-hood mental health. It diminishes the risk of sleep disorders and enhances psychosocial functioning and stress tolerance.

☐ Sleep training is not difficult. Sleep training comes naturally to most parents once they try it. The most important aspect of it is consistency. It may seem difficult in the first week of practicing it, but later down the road, it comes easy and convenient for an-yone in the household. Besides your partner, you may also have to persuade your other relative about the importance of sleep training. Make sure that you agree with your spouse, though. While you can proceed with the training without other members' approval, you must agree with your spouse before starting the sleep training as he will need to be directly involved. Try to explain the process and that in the long-term, the baby will be healthier, stronger, and cry less.

☐ Set the ground rules and agree with them.

☐ I see many moms struggling with dealing with relatives who keep disrupting baby's sleep despite being "warned" not to interrupt the progress. Understandably, they mean well by holding or rocking the baby the entire time while he is sleeping. They may not understand why you are doing what you are doing. Talking to them and explaining, for example, how holding the baby the entire time when he is sleeping is good at that moment. Still, it does not help him in the long run since he will become too dependent on it as that's the only way they are learning how to sleep and eventually refuse to sleep unless he is being held in arms.

While other household members may not be on board with sleep training, communicate with them about your decision, your expectations in terms of interruptions, distractions, and any disruptions they may cause. Both sides need to understand the baby's healthy sleep needs. You have chosen well in establishing significant and lasting healthy sleep habits for your child. As a parent, it is your responsibility to stand on what you think is important and beneficial to your child, so don't be afraid to advocate for your precious little treasure.

SLEEP REGRESSION

Your baby will go through many stages of development in her first year of life. The easiest noticeable evolutions will be in her sleep. Sometimes they will be pleasant surprises; other times, they will frustrate and annoy you.

You cannot prevent or predict how your baby will change from a deep sleeper to a fussy baby who cannot get shuteye for over thirty minutes, and vice versa. These occurrences are also known as sleep regressions.

Your baby may go through a sleep regression at some point in the first few months of life. It's not a pleasant thing for either you or the baby. However, keep in mind that these stages are only temporary and that there are ways you can make them seem less disturbing for everyone in your household.

What is a sleep regression?

Sleep regression is a period when the baby suddenly experiences sleep problems. It generally doesn't last over two weeks, and it usually seems worse during the night but can also be noticeable during the day when the baby has trouble napping, which enhances the stress for both her and the parents.

What causes sleep regression in babies, and why does it happen?

As I mentioned before, your child will go through sleep regression several times within her first year of life. Every time, there may be different factors that will cause her sleep problems. It may be one or more of the causes below:

- A growth spurt, which makes babies extra-hungry and more alert than usual.

- Teething pain, which makes her wake up often at night.
- Reaching a new developmental milestone, which excites her too much.

- Disruptions in routines, like starting daycare.

- Traveling, which inevitably involves sleeping in a new environment.

- An illness, such as a cold or an ear infection.

As surprising as sleep regression will happen, be able to identify its cause every single time.

- ## How long does sleep regression last?

Sleep regression may last between two and four weeks. Its duration depends on the baby and the development stage that she's going through. You should not stop sleep training while it occurs and try to ease your baby's discomfort with affection, playtime, and a calm, patient attitude.

- ## Signs of sleep regression

Like the duration of sleep regression, the signs of sleep regression differ from one baby to the next depending on the child's development stage. You may notice signs of sleep regression in your baby, such as:

- More frequent night waking

- Trouble falling asleep at bedtime

- Increased fussiness or crankiness

- Suddenly refusing to take naps

- Unusual refusal to eat before sleep

Many of these signs will happen overnight. You may have the strange impression that your child has turned into a completely different baby from one day to the next. Remember to be understanding, patient, and in control to not increase your baby's stress.

When do sleep regressions happen?

Sleep regression does not occur on an exact schedule. However, there are a few milestones that are foreseeable for most babies out there. Here are the most common ones!

- ## Eight Weeks

This is not a common regression, but when it happens, it is pretty short. At this age, a baby's melatonin hormones that he got from his mommy at birth are wearing off, and his melatonin hormones are not matured enough, and so we notice a more alert baby. Since the hormones regulate the baby's sleep and are now wearing off, the baby may have difficulty falling asleep on his own and begin developing a strong dependence on parents or sleep props. This is when it becomes imperative to be careful not to introduce any new bad habits to get the baby to sleep. Stick to your regular schedule, offer comfort but do not let the baby fall asleep in your arms or help him fall asleep. This is where the drowsiness but awake is critical to ensure that we can continue to help the baby learn how to fall asleep independently. Please help him be ready to sleep by staying consistent with his bedtime and nap time routines and paying close attention to his wake windows. With the baby being more alert, you may think that he is ok staying up for too long, but this can cause him to be overtired, which is a recipe for inconsolably intense crying if you ask me.

- **Three to Four Months**

This one is the most common of sleep regressions, and most probably, the worst one, too. Most parents hate it because they are taken by surprise exactly when their baby has gotten used to sleeping gently without crying or too much fussiness.

The cause of this sleep regression is reaching new milestones, including rolling over, flipping over, being more aware of his surrounding, and sometimes with pain associated with teething for some babies. Hunger linked to growth spurts and the excitement of rolling over for the first time can cause sleep problems.

Since the baby was born, he has been mainly in a swaddle in a crib during his sleep. If you left him on his back, he would stay in that position until you pick him up. And now it has happened! He is now a "big boy," he figured out how to roll over, and it's fun!!! He will practice the new trick as much as possible, even when you want him to take a break and go to sleep. Since he is a baby, he doesn't know when to stop, and so it will become a challenge when he keeps "practicing," meaning he stays awake, rolling over, and eventually gets tired. Being overtired comes the discomfort that the baby does not know how to respond to apart from crying and being unusually fussy and cranky. With this situation, it's easier for parents to get frustrated, exhausted, and confused. Stay patient and understand that the baby doesn't want to feel the way he may have felt, and try to help his experience go less overwhelming for him. Practice the new milestones more during the day, give him more affection and more time together when he is awake. Take him outside, to the park, around the block, or in the backyard to distract him from crying but also to burn that extra energy so he can be ready to sleep when it's bedtime. As always, avoid introducing bad habits out of desperation. The regression will be done before you know it if you stay consistent with the plan with a bit more patience and affection.

- **Six Months**

This stage of sleep regression is not as difficult as the one at four months. By this age, your baby should be able to sleep for most of the night. However, the regression mostly happens to babies who have not mastered sleeping independently and still need help to fall asleep. You may notice this more with frequent night waking, early morning waking, and trouble going to sleep at bedtime. The baby has now realized the effects of some of the surrounding actions. He refuses to sleep because he realized that if he cries, mommy or daddy will come to pick him up and help him go to sleep. Now is the right time to cement a suitable sleep training method since the baby's sleep cycles are mature enough, and the baby can follow healthy sleep habits.

- **Eight to Ten Months**

Just when you and your baby were settling into an efficient bedtime routine, sleep regression strikes again. This time, the excitement of crawling for the first time and separation anxiety can cause sleep troubles. Again, please stick to the regular routines, avoid introducing new bad habits and practice, practice and practice more during his awake time.

- **Twelve Months**

On the brink of her first anniversary, your baby will experience another stage of sleep regression. Around this mark, she will start standing up and exploring her environment better. This milestone can cause intense excitement and anxiety, which leads to sleep issues at night.

Toddlers also go through sleep regressions at around eighteen months and twenty-four months that may be caused by nightmares and night terrors, fear of the dark, toddler teething, and separation anxiety.

Overall Tips on How to Manage Sleep Regression in Your Baby

Fortunately, sleep regression is only temporary. You should be able to manage it easily by following common-sense tips, such as:

- Get to know and watch out for your baby's sleep cues.
- Stick to a consistent bedtime routine.
- Ensure your baby is getting enough sleep during the day.
- If your baby suddenly starts crying in the middle of the night, give her a few minutes to fuss before you respond for her to learn to fall asleep on her own.
- Avoid rocking or cuddling your baby at night, as this may encourage her to wake for your attention constantly.
- Consider sleep training if your baby is at least four to six months old or older and give it at least two weeks to see if it's working before changing to a new strategy. If your baby seems to experience too much stress or anxiety, try giving her more attention during the day and even more before naps and bedtime to help her feel more secure while sleeping.

Can You Prevent Sleep Regression?

Unfortunately, no, you cannot prevent this stage as it is a natural period in your baby's development. You can try to make it as easy to go through for the baby, for you, and for everyone in your household. Stick to a sleep training method and hang in there; you will be proud of yourself once this period comes to pass!

TEETHING

Sleep training usually starts slowly for most parents and babies out there. Then, it goes smoothly for a few weeks in a row, and everyone's happy. You even find it hard to believe that other parents struggle with this method.

Suddenly, it all goes wrong for no apparent reason. Your bundle of joy cannot get a peaceful rest for anything in the world. She is fussy, irritable, and often wakes up to cry at night. You cannot understand why until you see tiny, white pearls coming out of her gums. Teething has begun!

Most babies get their first tooth around the six-month mark. However, teething pain starts from as early as three months, and it comes and goes for most of the child's first year of life. Sometimes she can battle through it without too much trouble. Other times, she cannot spend thirty minutes without crying about it.

Teething symptoms include:

- Drooling
- Rash
- Coughing or gag reflex
- Biting
- Crying
- Irritability
- Refusing to eat
- Night waking
- Ear pulling and cheek rubbing

Teething can pose some problems for your baby's usual bedtime routine, often waking, and the inability to get a good night's rest to prevent your infant from following a healthy, predictable sleep schedule. As a result, your sleep training may encounter some serious obstacles. However, it does not mean that you have to pause or stop sleep training. Remember that your baby goes through various stages of development in her first year. Even without the teething pain, she would still change the number of hours that she needs to sleep or the times of the day when she requires shuteye.

You can continue with sleep training while your baby is teething. All you have to do is more patient and reward your child with more affection and quality time for her effort. Increase the quality of playtime hours throughout the day and take her out of her sleep environment. Daily strolls, playdates, visits to friends and relatives should distract her from her teething pain. It should also help her deplete her energy resources and enjoy a deeper sleep at night and nap time.

Daylight savings are tricky and cause sleep problems for adults. They may be even more troublesome for babies, especially if your baby is barely getting used to the differences between daytime and nighttime.

Daylight Saving Time (DST) takes place twice per year. It occurs once in March and again in October. Every time, it can cause noticeable trouble for your baby's usual sleep quality.

Your baby may wake up earlier than usual after DST, which might cause her to be irritable for the rest of the day. Alternatively, she may have trouble going to bed in the evening and falling asleep one or two hours later than usual. This time, she may wake up later the following day and feel groggy and fussy throughout the day.

It usually takes a few days for your baby to adjust to the new sleeping schedule after daylight savings. The good news is that the accommodation period is only temporary. Also, it will only take place twice in your baby's first year of life.

Here are a few tips to help your baby adjust to DST and not disturb the sleep training schedule too much during daylight saving times:

- **Adjust gradually.** It takes a few days for your baby to adjust to DST, so be patient during this time and help her transition gradually. Do not change her bedtime routine abruptly or disrupt her daytime napping rituals too quickly.

- If the clock is moving an hour forward, before two weeks of the actual daylight-saving change, balance the entire day schedule by fifteen mins later. Give it two days before changing to another fifteen mins later until you reach the desired one hour forward. If, for example, there will be Daylight saving to one hour forward in two weeks, we would start by adjusting the entire day schedule by fifteen minutes later. If the baby wakes typically up at 7:00 a.m., and the daylight saving will add on another hour to make it "7:00 a.m.," which will be "8:00 a.m." for the baby's internal clock, before two weeks, we will increase the time by fifteen minutes. If the baby wakes up at 7:00 a.m., we will wait to pick him up until 7:15 a.m. Make sure that the room is entirely dark to avoid the sunlight from waking him up. **Delay every activity during the day by fifteen mins including feeding times, nap times, playing times, bath times, and bedtimes.** Give it two to three days before adding another fifteen minutes. Meaning that on day three, you will pick him up at 7:30 a.m. You can adjust as fast or as slow as you think your baby is responding to the timing, and in as comfortable minutes, you and the baby will wait (five, ten, fifteen, or thirty mins delay). Some babies will be fully adjusted to the new time change within four days, and some may take up to two weeks.

- Do the same for the Daylight saving when one hour is moved backward. **This time reduces the whole day schedule (feeding, naps, activities, bedtime) to fifteen minutes early.** If baby wakes up at 7:00 a.m. and this time will be 6:00 a.m. for the new time change, we will have to wake him up at 15 minutes earlier (I know! Not fun, but it will pay off within a few days, and you won't have to deal with a regression caused by the daylight savings). Meaning that if the baby typically wakes up at 7:00 a.m., you wake him up at 6:45 a.m. and adjust the rest of the day's schedule to fifteen minutes earlier. Since we want the baby towage up fifteen minutes early this time, instead of keeping the room dark in the morning, open the blinds or curtains for the light to come in the room. This will help the baby's internal clock adjust faster since light means being awake to the baby's internal clock.

- **Stick to the usual bedtime routine.** Even if you change the clocks, it doesn't mean that you need to change the bedtime routine. Keep the same ritual before napping and sleep; start it early or later according to the time change.

- **Keep bedtime duration the same.** Daylight saving times may confuse for both adults and children. Whether you turn the clock one hour behind or forward, maintain the same hours for naps or nighttime sleep.

- **Make the room darker or increase the light.** Your baby's internal clock will not understand why the dawn and dusk times differ in light and darkness from one day to another during DST. You can ease the confusion by making the room darker on spring evenings and increasing the light on fall nights. You should do the opposite in the mornings for each season. Use blackout curtains, blinds to ensure that the room is entirely dark that you cannot see your hand (Yes, that dark!) in the mornings when you need the baby to wake up later and open blinds or curtains in mornings you want the baby to wake up earlier.

- **Keep the same duration for naps.** Some parents may shorten or lengthen the duration of their babies' daytime naps during DST. You should avoid doing so because it might create more nighttime sleep problems, such as an overtired baby. After all, he had brief naps or a baby who is not ready to sleep at night since he had long stretches of a nap.

- **Shorten the routine if you have to.** I mentioned you should maintain the same bedtime routine. However, if you notice that your baby gets tired quicker than usual during daylight saving time, shorten it without taking the usual elements from it. It means that you should still bathe her, play with her, sing her lullabies, and every other ritual in your bedtime routine. However, try to make them shorter. This way, your baby will not become overtired and have problems falling asleep.

SICKNESS

In her first year of life, your baby will go through various experiences. Some of them will be exciting and joyful. Unfortunately, others will be frightful and unsettling, like a sickness, for example.

Whether it is a minor cold or a feverish state from teething, you can hardly avoid your baby becoming sick in her first twelve months or even in her next toddler stage. During this time, her illness may disturb your attempt to sleep training your child. Depending on her health condition, you may have to pause or end the training method altogether.
Here are a few guidelines that should help you make a simple decision about your baby's sleep training progress if she gets sick!

- **Evaluate her condition**

Sleep training is all about consistency. You find a suitable sleep training method for your baby, and you stick to it. She may protest it by crying or being moody and cranky. You should continue with the bedtime rituals, napping schedule, and nighttime sleeping. In a few days, she should respond positively to the habits you establish.

If you have begun sleep training your baby and notice she has a fever, abort your plan immediately. There is no use to make your child go through more trouble and confusion when she is sick or feeling under the weather. Once she gets better, you can start the training again from the beginning.

However, if you are at least a week or more into sleep training and your baby gets a cold, continue with the training plan as best as you can. Adjust her sleeping rituals and schedules to not interfere too much with her illness and battle through it until your baby recovers.
- **Maintain as many elements from the routine as possible.** If your child is only ill, try to maintain as many parts of her bedtime ritual as possible. You might shorten them a bit to increase her comfort as she recovers from the sickness. If the illness is trou-

blesome, and the pediatrician recommends fever-reducing medicine, use that to comfort your child. The medicine might make her feel sleepy more often, which may disrupt her napping schedule, but still try to stick to the daily routine as much as you can.

If your baby becomes dehydrated, has a fever, or any other unusual situation, immediately stop the sleep training routine, tend to your child according to your pediatrician, and resume it later when the baby is feeling well.

While your baby is sick, give up on the part in the sleep training routine where you don't address her needs immediately. She might go through discomfort, so try to comfort her as soon as possible and monitor her condition at all times.

As my rule of thumps, never sleep train a baby who has had a fever in the past twenty-four to forty-eight hours, and wait to resume the sleep training after the baby has been fever-free for forty-eight hours. Even if the baby is already sleep trained and worry about losing all the significant sleep improvements, if symptoms are still present, always respond to them and reduce how much you help the baby fall asleep.

TRAVELING

You should not put sleep training your baby on pause to travel . Again, you should not delay or cancel necessary traveling only to keep the sleep training program up and running. Sometimes, you have to travel and sleep train your baby at the same time.

Here is how you can continue sleep training and enjoying life on the road at the same time!

- **Mimic your bedtime routine.**

You cannot explain traveling to your baby and expect her to understand. You should not be surprised to see her becoming fussy and crying when you take her from her usual environment to entirely new ones. However, you can soothe her anxiety and calm her down by mimicking the bedtime routine you have at home. Regardless of where you are, try to keep the same feed-play-sleep sequence as you would do if you were in her nursery.

- **Don't leave home without the baby's soothing objects.**

One of the worst things that can happen when traveling and sleep training your baby is not having any soothing objects with you.

Babies grow fond of various things that they find soothing in their first year of life. Your child can find great comfort in a lovey, a blanket, a toy, and even in the white noise machine or her bedsheets. Even things that smell like a home might do the trick. Try to pack these soothers in your bag before hitting the road. They will come in handy later when your bundle of joy becomes fussy and cranky.

- **Do a trial run.**

If you have to travel for more than a few days or weeks with a baby during sleep training, you should first make a trial trip to see how she adapts to it. Try going to a friend or a relative's house just one night before the big trip. You will see how your baby reacts and what she finds soothing when her anxiety increases. Also, try letting your baby sleep in a travel crib at home for the few nights leading up to your trip, so he's used to it by the time you depart.

☐ **Stay at a hotel.** It might be a good idea to book a hotel when traveling and sleep training your baby at the same time. This way, you will have more control over her bedtime routine and napping rituals. Also, you will not disturb your family or friends too much.

☐ **When to put sleep training on hold.** When traveling, try to stick to your sleep training schedule as much as possible. However, sometimes this goal may seem almost impossible to achieve. Maybe on your upcoming travel, your baby goes through teething, fever, and sleep regression at the same time.

If your baby becomes nearly impossible to soothe, and all the bedtime rituals are exacerbating the situation, maybe it would be a good idea to put sleep training on hold. You don't have to abort it entirely and lose all the progress that your baby has made so far. You only put it on pause and resume it when you get home or when you have more control over her bedtime routine.

PACIFIER DEPENDENCE

Babies zero to six months old can benefit from using pacifiers since they can help reduce risks of Sudden Infant Death Syndrome (SIDS). They may help soothe babies under three months old since they are still too young to soothe themselves effectively. To avoid side effects from prolonged use of pacifiers, such as the increased risk of middle ear infection, dental problems, disrupting breastfeeding, and dependence causing sleep troubles, I always advise to ditch pacifiers for babies six months and older.

For babies who are already too dependent on pacifiers, breaking the habit can be challenging and lead to intense crying. There are two ways you may go about breaking pacifier dependence if it is disrupting your baby's sleep.

- **Cold turkey:** You choose a time to ditch the pacifiers and promise yourself not to resort to them again. If the baby is big enough to understand, you may ask him to help you throw them in a trash. I know it sounds harsh, but you may explain to your child that it's time to throw them away because "they are for babies and we are big now and don't need them anymore or that they are yucky." By involving a child, they will be more understanding since they will know that the pacifiers are gone and cannot come back. Now be careful and do this when the child is in good spirits and maybe get him a new lovey or blankie to distract him from pacifiers if he remembers about it later. You may use either the cold turkey method for younger babies, and they forget about it pretty quickly, or use a gradual approach if you think they have a hard time adjusting.

☐ **Gradual approach**: if the baby won't go to sleep unless they are sucking on a pacifier, start by gradually taking it away. When the baby is about to fall asleep, try to take it away before he is fully asleep and aim to take it away when he is a little more awake than the last time to fall asleep slightly on his own. And he will eventually fall asleep without sucking on the pacifier.

APPENDIX

Great job choosing to give your baby the precious gift of sleep! Sleep is vital in growing babies and choosing to establish healthy sleep habits in their early stage of life will set a good foundation for other desired behaviors such as reaching their age-appropriate milestones, less crying and more happiness, easier going baby, more likely to socialize with others. It is also about enjoying raising an independent and confident little being who is ready to try more things since they are more alert, and have better cognitive performance. You have also chosen well for yourself! With a healthy, happy well-rested baby, you are sure to have more peace of mind, more time to work on that project that has been stuck in your computer folder, more time and flexibility to keep that healthy body in shape, and how about more date nights and restful nights? You are your baby's best advocate! Stay strong, be fierce, trust your "mommy instinct", and don't hesitate to ask for help or seek advice no matter how uncomfortable it may be.

As I always say; motherhood is a learning process and your uniqueness brings in a special flavor to it!

INDEX

Self-soothing, 74

Avoid these sleep training obstacles, 71

BABY CRYING DIFFEREN-TIATIONS, 15

baby is hungry, 24

Baby monitor-, 75

baby's clinginess gradually, 25

baby's internal clock, 18

baby's schedule, 91

baby's temperament, 20

bedtime ritual, 27, 106

bedtime routine, 18, 19, 20, 21, 22, 23, 24, 25, 27, 28, 29, 31, 33, 35, 41, 51, 52, 53, 54, 55, 57, 58, 62, 63, 68, 69, 71, 74, 81, 87, 88, 92, 94, 99, 100, 102, 103, 104, 105, 107, 108

BEDTIME ROUTINE, 51

Bedtime Strategy, 82

Benefits of Easy Daily Planning, 47

Benefits of sleep training your baby, 9

CHECKLIST BEFORE SLEEP TRAINING, 72

child's fear of desertion, 26

circadian rhythm, 28

Colic, 17

comfortable clothes, 23

Communication Milestones, 61

conducive quiet sleeping environment, 18

CONDUCIVE SLEEP ENVI-RONMENT, 48

Confidence-Boosting, 76

cope with changes, 4

crying, 1, 3, 4, 5, 8, 13, 15, 16, 17, 20, 21, 22, 23, 24, 54, 73, 76, 77, 78, 83, 85, 89, 92, 94, 98, 99, 100, 101, 105, 107, 108, 110, 119

Day and Night Confusion, 28

Daylight Saving, 66, 102

DEALING WITH HOUSE-HOLD MEMBERS WHO DISAGREE, 93

Differentiating a Hunger Feeding vs a Comfort Feeding, 80

Drowsiness but Awake, 30

EARLY WAKINGS STRAT-EGY, 89

Effective Bedtime Routine, 53

Eighteen to Twenty-Four Months, 68

eye contact, 17, 36, 54, 61, 74, 76, 83

Feeding Milestones, 61

fussy cry, 16

Going to Bed Awake, 58

growth spurt, 21, 96

How Do I Put My Baby Down Awake, 57

how to put your baby down to sleep while he is still drowsy, 31

instincts, 7
lamentation, 18
levels of light and darkness, 23
Listening, 39
Long-distance traveling, 22
lullaby, 19, 25, 55
Manage Sleep Regression, 100
massage, 17
Melatonin, 28
**Milestones by Age 0 - 36
Months**, 59
MINDSET & READINESS,
71
MOM'S GUILT, 5
Motor Milestones, 60
Nap Training, 88
Night Wakings Strategy, 85
Nine to Twelve Months, 65
non-feeding waking,, 85
Non-REM Sleep Stage, 30
ON BEING PERFECT, 7
or disruption in her routine, 22
Overtired babies, 18
PACIFIER DEPENDENCE,
108
predictability, 27, 52
problematic behavior, 17
protesting/upset cry:, 86
Quiet time, 21
Rapid-Eye Movement Sleep, 29
reasons for your child's tan-
trum, 18
**REASONS WHY BABIES
STRUGGLE TO SLEEP,**
18
REM Sleep, 29
Safe Sleeping, 7, 34

**Schedule Sample for 0-3-
Months-Old Babies**, 41
**Schedule Sample for Three to
Six-Months Old Babies**, 43
SCHEDULES, 41
Sensory Milestones, 61
separation anxiety, 26, 36, 67,
68, 69, 99, 100
SHORT NAPS, 89
SICKNESS, 105
**SIGNS THAT BABY IS NOT
GETTING ENOUGH
SLEEP**, 31
Sleep Independently, 78
Sleep props, 19
sleep regression, 21, 22, 52,
63, 66, 96, 97, 98, 99, 100,
108
SLEEP REGRESSION, 95
sleep regression stage, 22
Sleep Tips for Infants, 35
Sleep Tips for Newborns, 35
sleep training, 4, i, 1, 2, 3, 4, 5,
8, 9, 16, 29, 30, 37, 40, 43,
47, 48, 50, 59, 60, 61, 62, 63,
64, 66, 68, 71, 78, 90, 91, 93,
94, 95, 97, 99, 100, 101, 102,
103, 105, 106, 107, 108, 119
**Sleep Training Misconcep-
tions**, 7, 8
sleeping goals, i
sleep-wake cycle, 20
soothing methods, 18
sound machine, 74
teething, 22
TEETHING, 101
Teething symptoms, 101

temperament, 3, 20, 37, 119
temperature in your room, 24
Ten Points During Sleep Training, 73
The ABC Rule, 49
The Do's and Don'ts of Sleep Training, 46
The Fussy Cry, 16
The Protesting Cry, 16
the step-by-step process, 4
Thirty to Thirty-Six Months, 69
to age-appropriate wake periods, 18
TRAVELING, 106

tricky cries, 82
tummy time, 24, 63, 74
Twelve to Eighteen Months, 66
Twenty-four to Thirty Months, 68
unfamiliar environment, 23
vulnerabilities, 7
WAKE TIMES, 40
whine, 25
Will my baby cry, 3
Witching Hour, 17
with five sleep stages, 29

RESSOURCES

When it comes to baby sleep resources, below are some of my favorites and the ones that my clients also loved! You can also find more healthy baby sleep tips on my website at www.serenesleepconsulting.com. Other websites include:

- AAP.org
- sleepfoundation.org
- nichd.nih.gov

More baby and parenting related books:
- *Bringing up Bébé* by Pamela Druckerman
- *The Happiest Baby on the Block*; Fully revised and Updated Second Edition by Harvey Karp
- *How Parents Can Raise Resilient Children* by Frank Dixon

Favorite bedtime baby books :

- *Goodnight Moon* by Margaret Wise Brown
- *Bonsoir Lune / Goodnight Moon* (French Edition) by Margaret Wise Brown
- *I Love You to the Moon and Back* by Amelia Hepworth
- *The Wonderful Things You Will Be* by Emily Winfield Martin
- *Good Night, Little Blue Truck* by Alice Schertle

REFERENCES

Pennestri, M. H., Laganière, C., Bouvette-Turcot, A.A., Pokhvisneva, I., Steiner, M., Meaney, M. J., Gaudreau, H., & Mavan Research Team (2018). Uninterrupted Infant Sleep, Development, and Maternal Mood. Retrieved from:
https://pediatrics.aappublications.org/content/142/6/e20174330

Pacheco, D. September 2020. Children and Sleep. Retrieved from:
https://www.sleepfoundation.org/children-and-sleep

CDC, Centers for Disease Control and Prevention. (2018). Safe Sleep for Babies. Retrieved from: https://www.cdc.gov/vitalsigns/safesleep/index.html

Ma, D. March 2009. Check cribs for defects before placing babies back to sleep. Retrieved from https://www.aappublications.org/content/30/3/29.7

Dr. Karp, H. (2020). The 5 S's for Soothing Babies. Retrieved from:
https://www.happiestbaby.com/blogs/baby/the-5-s-s-for-soothing-babies

Suni, E. September 24, 2020. How Much Sleep Do Babies and Kids Need? Retrieved from:
https://www.sleepfoundation.org/children-and-sleep/how-much-sleep-do-kids-need

HealthyChildren.org. (2018). Getting Your Baby to Sleep. Retrieved from:
https://www.healthychildren.org/English/ages-stages/baby/sleep/Pages/getting-your-baby-to-sleep.aspx

NIH, National Institutes of Health. Aug 12, 2019. Mom's Mental Health Matters: Partners, Family, and Friends. Retrieved from: https://www.nichd.nih.gov/ncmhep/initiatives/moms-mental-health-matters/partners-family-friends

ACKNOWLEDGMENTS

Thank you so much to all the babies and all the families who allowed me the honor to help their precious ones to sleep better. It is rewarding to see a family get back their sanity, calmness, their confidence, more work done, and more importantly, to get restful nights that they so much need and deserve. You called me many sweet names such as "The Sleep Fairy" or a "Godsend," and your smiles and happiness continue to drive me!

Thank you to my family and friends who don't cease to show me love and support!

To my beautiful children Obinna and Nerisse, and to my loving husband Henry, I love you!

ABOUT THE AUTHOR

GHISLAINE NNAJI

Website: www.serenesleepconsulting.com
Email: support@serenesleepconsulting.com

Ghislaine Nnaji is a pediatric sleep consultant, founder of The *"Tantrums No More"* program, and Host of *"A Serene Baby Sleep" Podcast*. With her background in Health Sciences, Ghislaine developed a keen interest in babies' behaviors and how sleep plays a major role in the overall attitude or wellbeing of the babies. For years, she has worked with countless families, helping them to find the right approach unique to their baby's temperament and to their lifestyle preferences. With many sleep training methods only focusing on the baby and leaving out the parents mental readiness in implementing and learning how, why and what to do during which situation, she realized that helping new parents understand precisely why they are doing, feeling, and reacting the way they may be responding and understanding the root cause of the baby's sleep trouble is the best long-lasting solution to establishing life-long healthy habits of good sleep. Knowing that no parent likes to hear a crying baby for hours, she developed a program that uses gentle and effective strategies without resorting to "cry-it-out" methods. You can learn more about her services at serenesleepconsulting.com. Ghislaine has been featured in different major sites such as on ABC, CBS, FOX, NBC, and many more. A native of Rwanda, she now lives in San Francisco with her husband and their two children (a boy and a girl). When she is not helping babies to sleep better or not on "mommy duty", Ghislaine enjoys jogging around a neighborhood lake, improvised dance shows with her husband and kids at home, trying out new recipes as she is also an avid advocate for healthy eating, and hearing all the happy stories from her clients. Ghislaine speaks English, French, Kinyarwanda and Swahili.

Printed in Poland
by Amazon Fulfillment
Poland Sp. z o.o., Wrocław

14589362R00076